# LEARN AS YOU PLAY CLARINET

BY PETER WASTALL

Revised edition 1989

**Learn As You Play** is a series of instrumental tutors designed specifically to prepare pupils for the early grades of all the principal examination boards. The tutors are suitable for both individual and group instruction.

The course, which is divided into 24 units, places the maximum emphasis on the early development of musicianship. From the beginning it introduces the student to a wide range of music, including works by leading contemporary composers. Each unit contains the following teaching programme:

1
New material is presented in clear progressive steps

2
Short, concise exercises enable new skills to be quickly developed

3
Instrumental solos by distinguished composers stimulate and develop practice repertoire

4
Progressive technical studies gradually bring the student into contact with specific instrumental technique

5
Instrumental duets (alternate units) provide experience in ensemble playing. Keyboard accompaniments to the duets can be added in early units

Progress is measured at eight-unit intervals by the introduction of Concert Pieces which utilise all previously learned material

Piano accompaniments are available for these pieces in a separate accompaniment book. The Concert Pieces are works representative of examination requirements and in many instances are works which have been set in current or past syllabuses.

SERIES EDITOR
PETER WASTALL



ISBN 0 85162 054 X

## Mouthpiece and ligature

To assemble the mouthpiece align the mouthpiece, barrel and top joint so that the reed is in a direct line with the back thumb hole. The ligature should be positioned about 4mm below the beaked section of the mouthpiece.

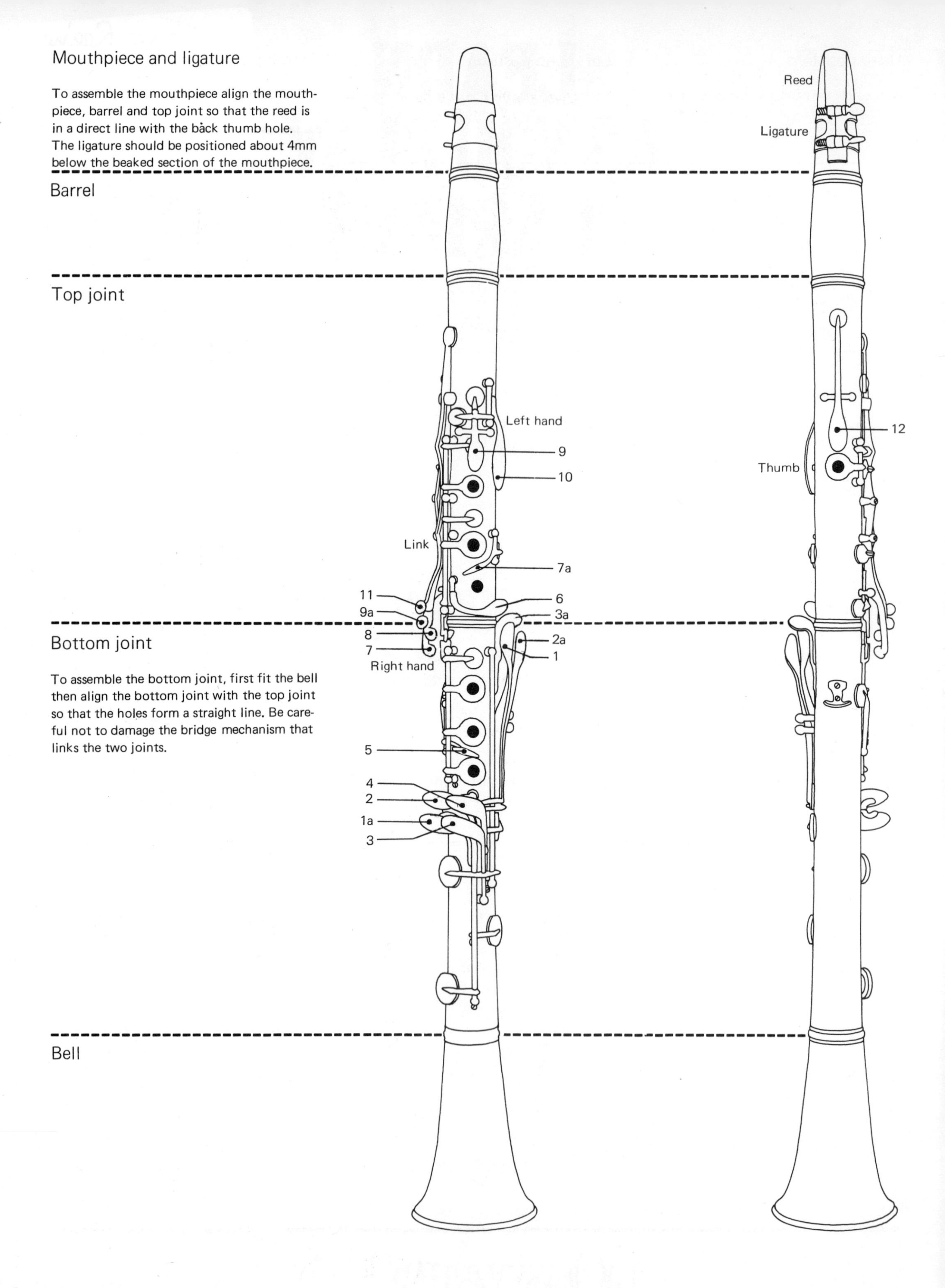


## Barrel

## Top joint

## Bottom joint

To assemble the bottom joint, first fit the bell then align the bottom joint with the top joint so that the holes form a straight line. Be careful not to damage the bridge mechanism that links the two joints.

## Bell

## Hand positions

Notice how the hand positions allow the fingers to curve naturally over the holes.

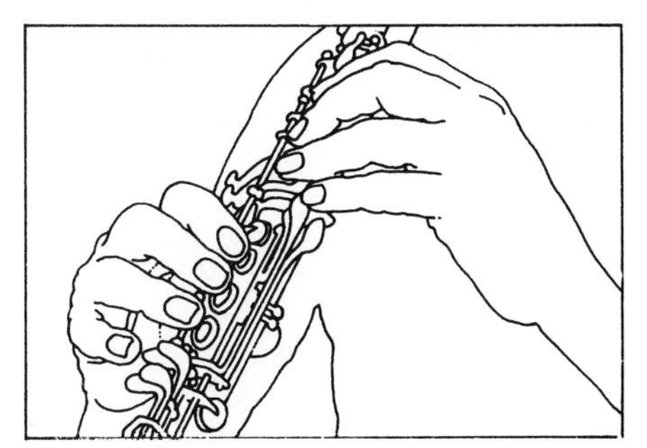

## Left hand position

Notice how only the side of the first finger top joint touches key 9 when playing A (unit 5).

## Thumb position

Notice that the left thumb is positioned nearly at right angles to the clarinet with the pad of the thumb covering the hole.

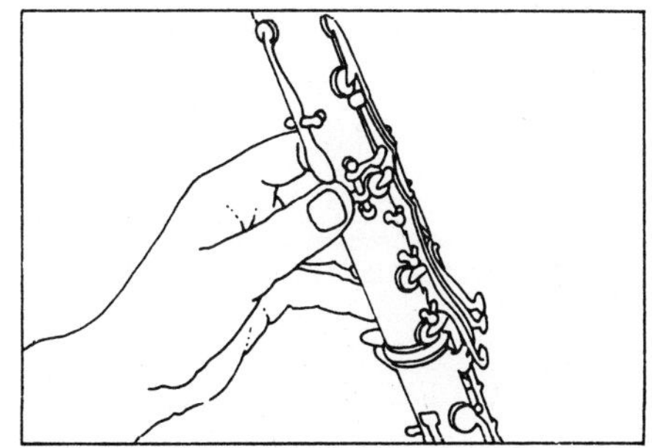

## Reed assembly

To fit the reed, lightly moisten it in your mouth, then place it on the mouthpiece (flat side of reed to flat side of mouthpiece). The thin tip of the reed should be even with the tip of the mouthpiece with just a hairline of mouthpiece showing.

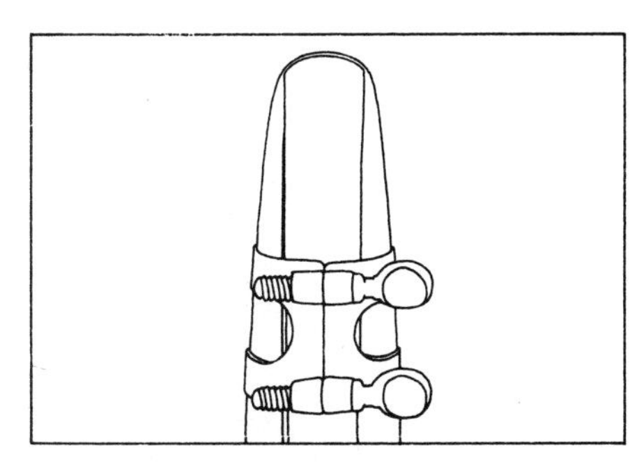

Using the finger chart as a guide, compare the sounds of C, D, E and F

## Position of teeth

The lower lip (2) is usually more advanced on the mouthpiece than the upper lip (1).

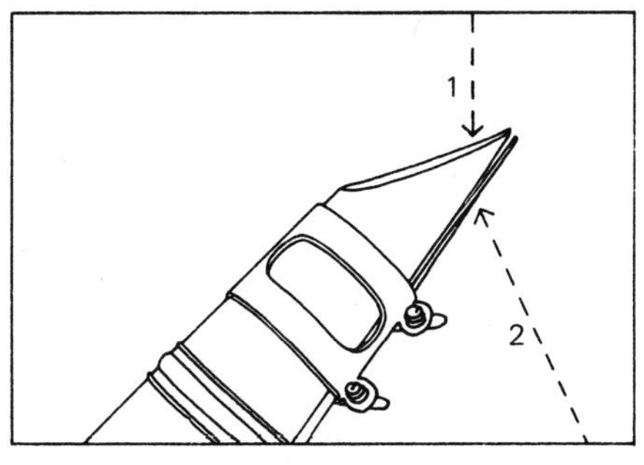


Try to start each note with a tongue movement similar to that used when pronouncing the letter 'T'.

## Embouchure

Notice how the lips form smoothly around the mouthpiece, with a little 'red' of the lower lip just showing.

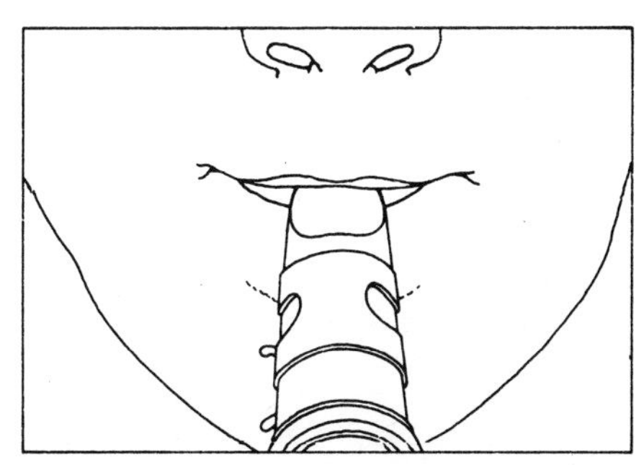

When tonguing, the tongue should touch the underside of of the reed, near the tip.

Closed ●
Open ○

| | | C | D | E | F |
|---|---|---|---|---|---|
| Left hand | Thumb | ● | ● | ● | ● |
| | First finger | ● | ● | ● | ○ |
| | Second finger | ● | ● | ○ | ○ |
| | Third finger | ● | ○ | ○ | ○ |
| Right hand | First finger | ○ | ○ | ○ | ○ |
| | Second finger | ○ | ○ | ○ | ○ |
| | Third finger | ○ | ○ | ○ | ○ |

# PREPARATORY MATERIAL FOR UNIT 1

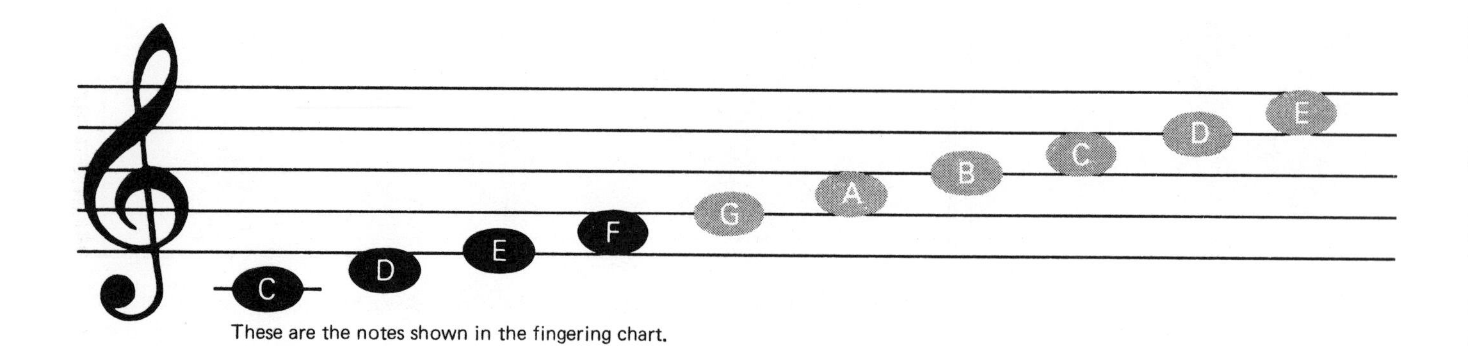


These are the notes shown in the fingering chart.

## Notation

Printed notes are also named after the first seven letters of the alphabet. From the example it can be seen that they are placed on a staff (the name of the five lines), each line and each space counting as one letter name.

## The Treble Clef

Since the same seven letter names are used for all instruments (i.e. those that produce low notes, as well as those that produce high notes) a clef sign is placed at the beginning of each staff to establish exact pitch. Music for the clarinet uses the treble clef.

## Note Lengths

The length of time a note is played is measured by the beat; the difference in length being shown by various types of note. The three types used in unit 1 are:

crotchet minim semibreve

Play the following crotchets trying to hold each for exactly the same amount of time.

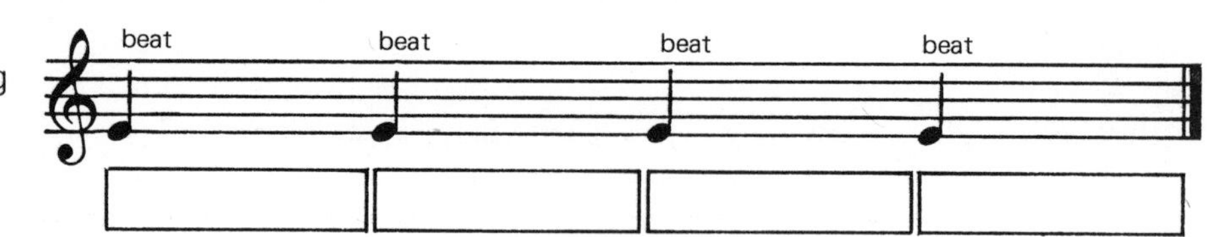


Now play the following minims, holding each note for the whole of beats one and two added together.

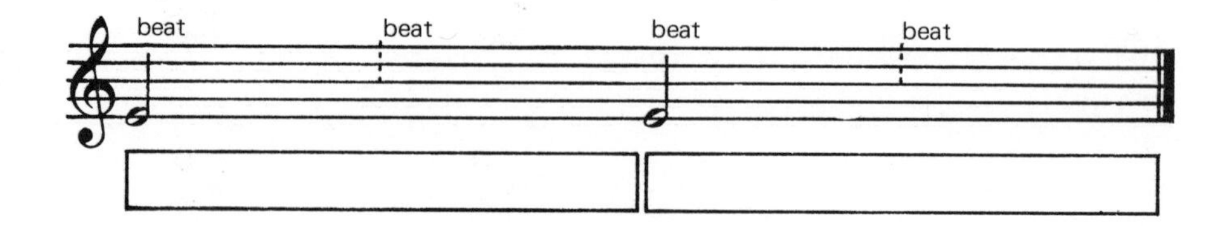


Now play a semibreve, trying to hold the note for exactly four beats.

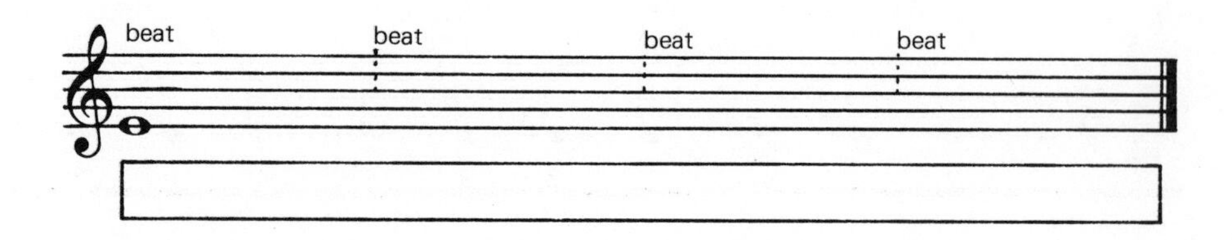

## Bars and bar lines

Bar line

Double bar line

Beats usually group themselves into regular patterns of either two, three or four; to show these patterns, the music is divided by bar lines into bars.

A double bar-line is used to separate differing sections of music within a single piece.

A thin/thick double bar indicates the end of a piece or exercise.

## Time Signatures

A time-signature is placed at the beginning of each piece of music to show how many beats there are in a bar, and the type of note that equals one beat. It is printed in fractional form, the value of the crotchet being shown as a fraction of a semibreve.

$\frac{2}{4}$ showing 2 crotchet beats in each bar

$\frac{3}{4}$ showing 3 crotchet beats in each bar

$\frac{4}{4}$ showing 4 crotchet beats in each bar

# UNIT 1

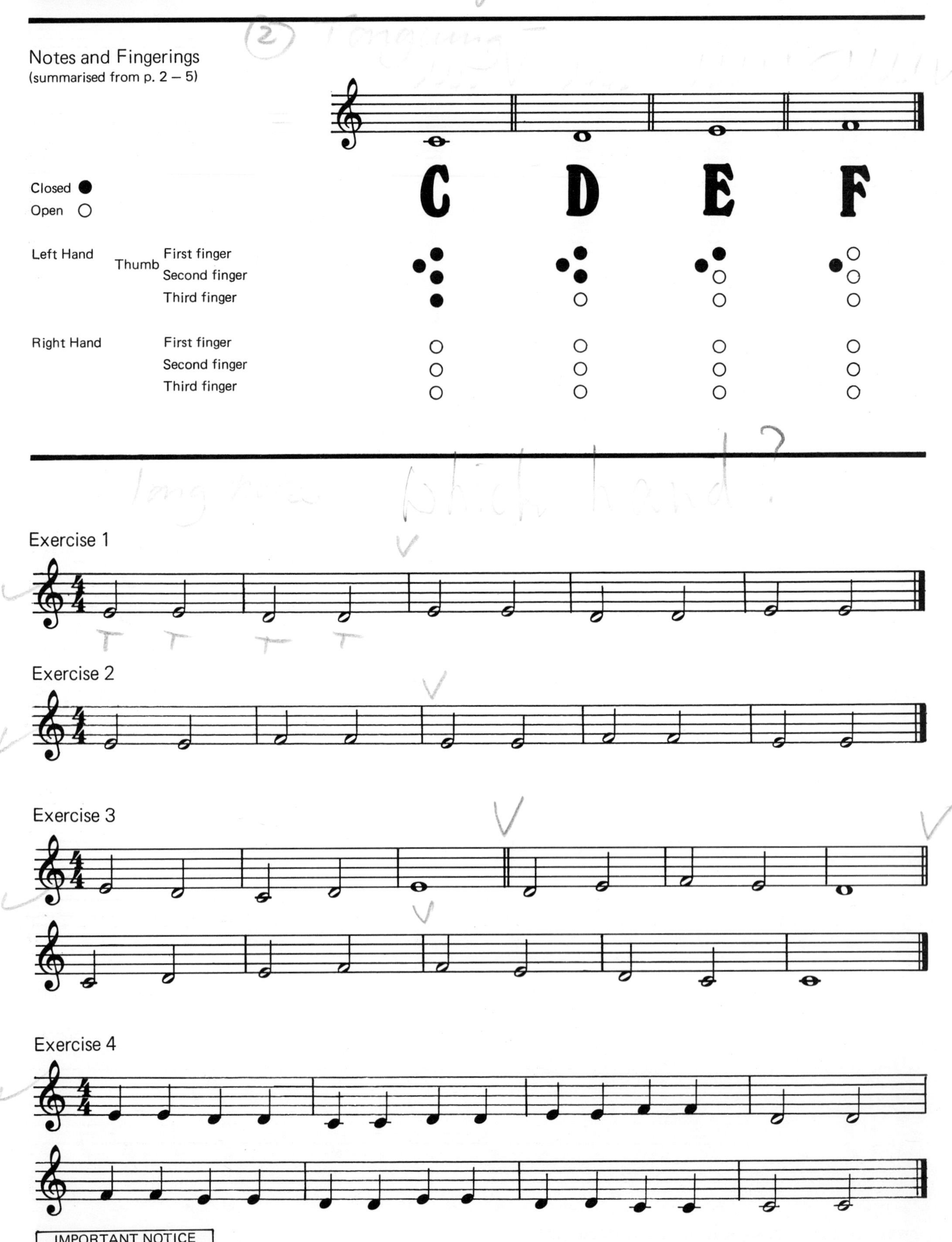
Notes and Fingerings
(summarised from p. 2 – 5)
C
D
E
F
Closed ●
Open ○
Left Hand
Thumb
First finger
Second finger
Third finger
Right Hand
First finger
Second finger
Third finger
Exercise 1
Exercise 2
Exercise 3
Exercise 4

Exercise 5

## Musicianship

When you practise the instrumental solos, notice how the notes form patterns almost as if they were words in a rhyme. In music these note patterns are called phrases; to help to identify them, phrases in this first unit have been marked with brackets. Breaths are normally taken at the ends of phrases; additional breaths can be taken, but these must be discreet so as not to disturb the natural flow of the phrase.

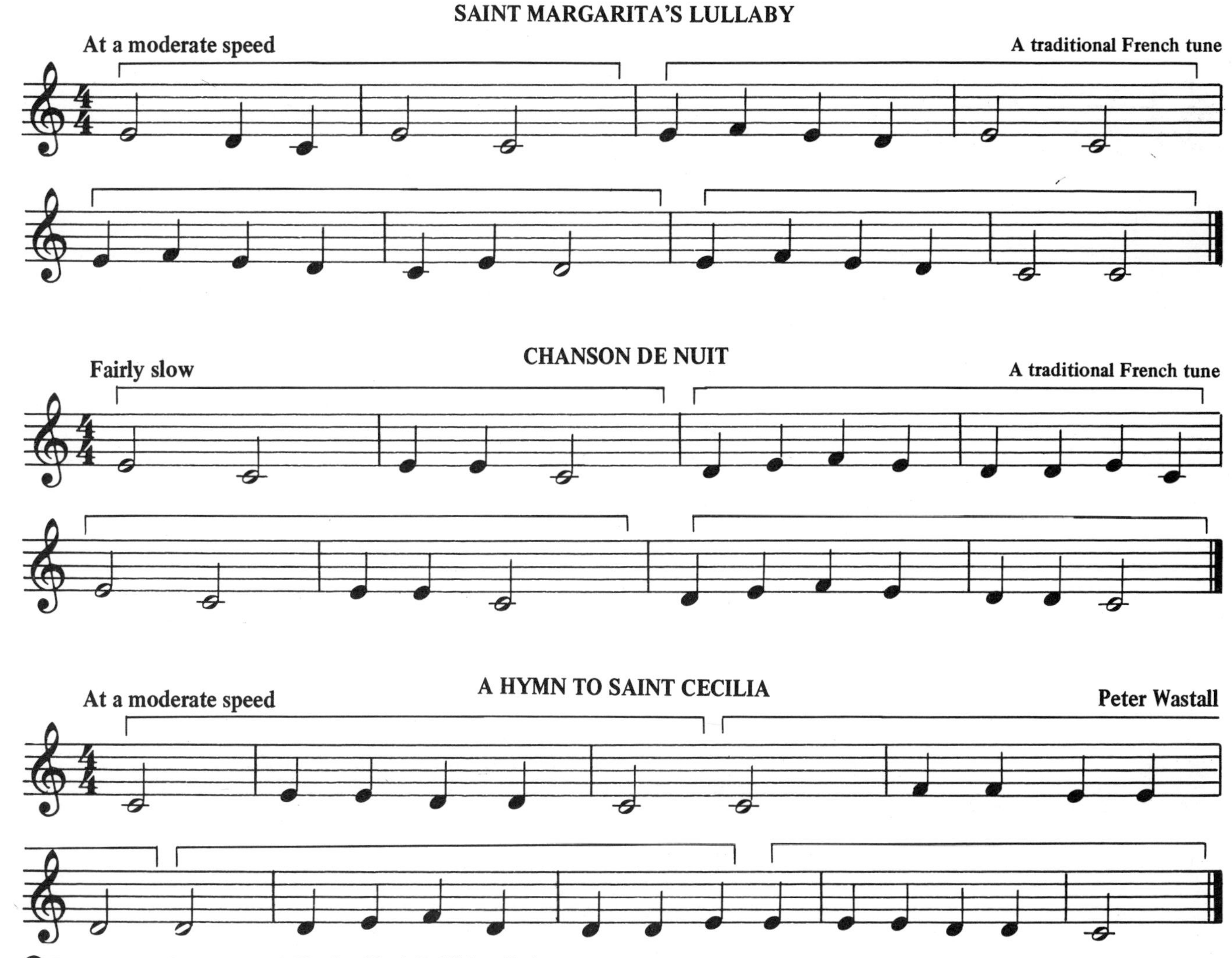

# UNIT 2

The Pause Sign

When a pause sign is placed over a note, the beat stops and the note is played for a period of time longer than its printed value. During the first section of this book the pause will be used mainly in the exercises, identifying individual notes that are to be sustained for as long as possible.

Rests

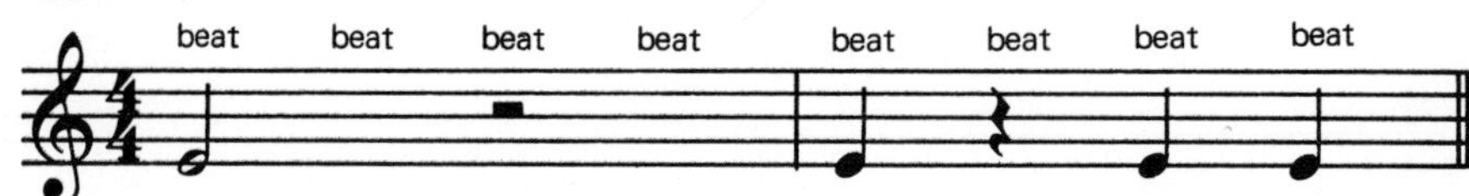


The length of time in which notes are not played is shown by various rests, each note having an equivalent rest. The example shows the minim rest (two beats of silence) and the crotchet rest (one beat of silence).

Exercise 1

Exercise 2

Exercise 3

## Tone development

One of the best ways to develop a full tone is to play individual long notes. In the exercise that follows, carry out the following drill.

1. Listen closely to the sound, aiming for a full, even tone.
2. Check the embouchure formation; remember that the contact point (the point where the lower lip firms against the reed) is crucial to good tone production.
3. Check the amount of mouthpiece that is inside the mouth; usually the top teeth rest on the beak section about six millimetres from the tip.
4. Check that the diaphragm is giving a light support to the air stream.

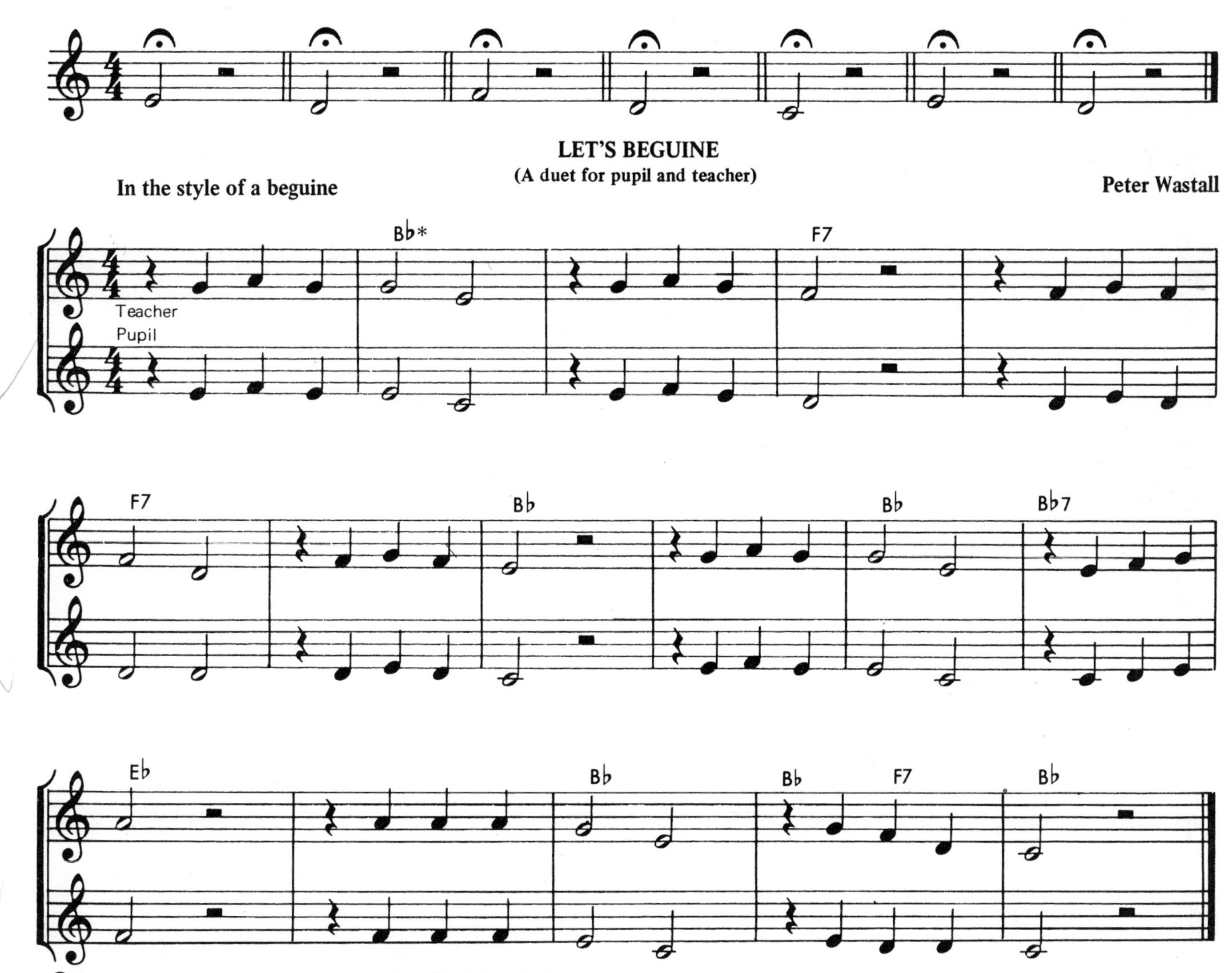




*Concert pitch chord symbols for keyboard accompaniment

# UNIT 3

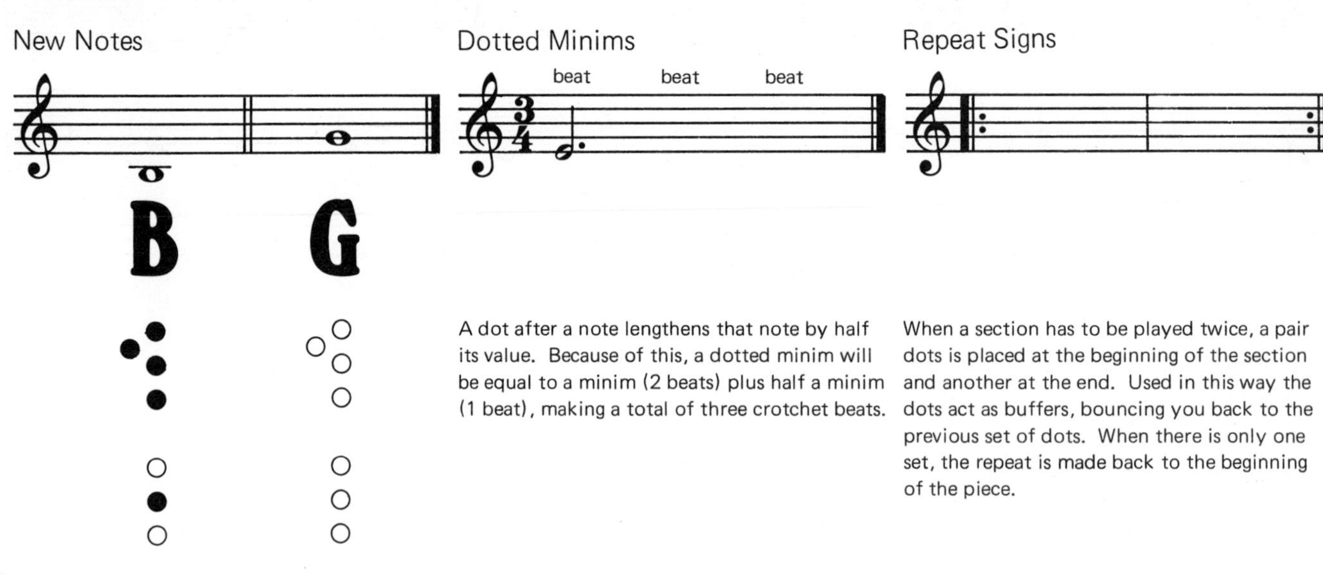


A dot after a note lengthens that note by half its value. Because of this, a dotted minim will be equal to a minim (2 beats) plus half a minim (1 beat), making a total of three crotchet beats.

When a section has to be played twice, a pair dots is placed at the beginning of the section and another at the end. Used in this way the dots act as buffers, bouncing you back to the previous set of dots. When there is only one set, the repeat is made back to the beginning of the piece.

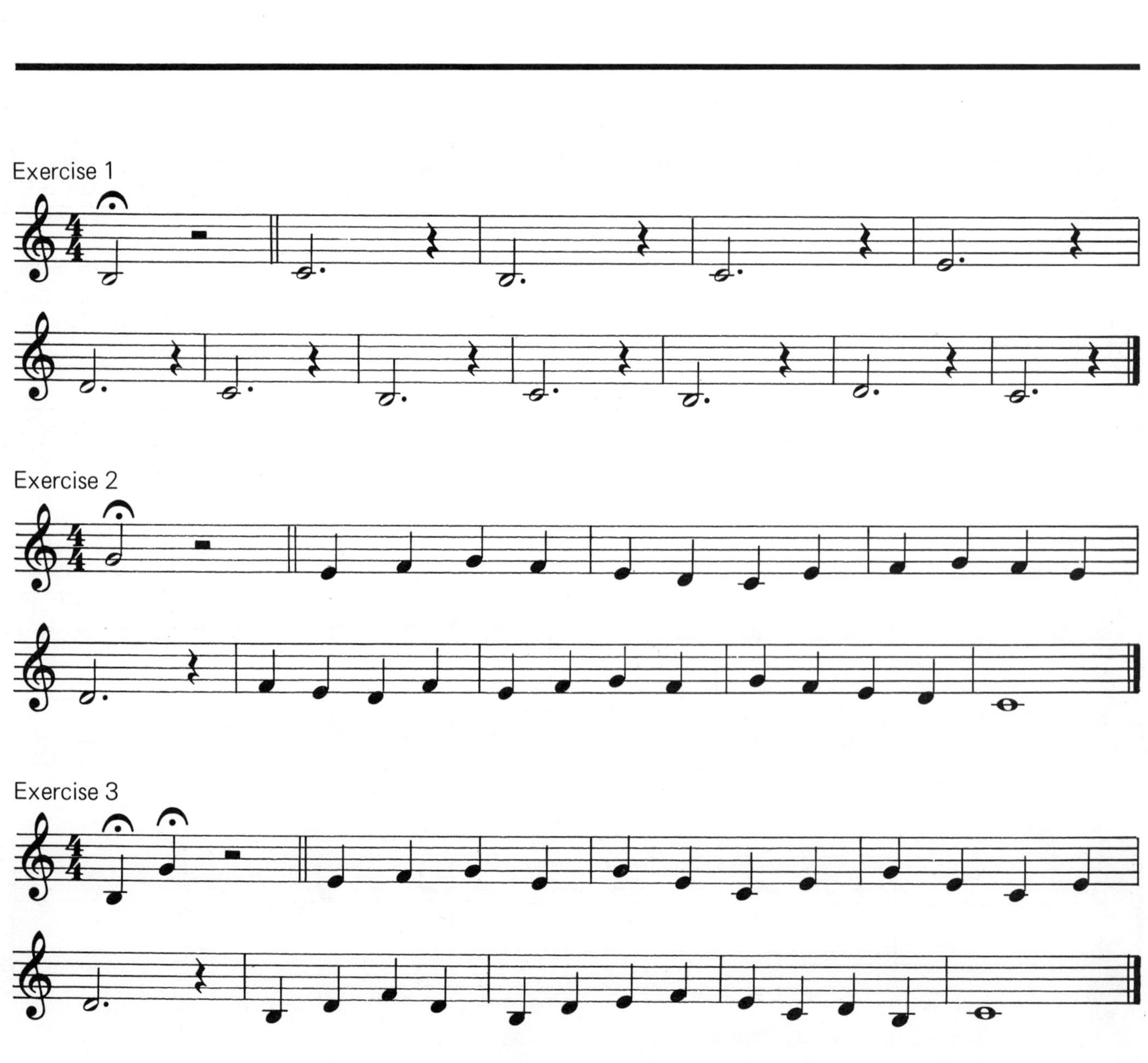

## Musicianship

The ability to remember melodic phrases plays an important part in the development of musicianship. To help develop a melodic memory, try each week to memorise one of the shorter instrumental solos.

The grade 1 aural tests issued by the Associated Board of the Royal Schools of Music will help memory development and should be incorporated into the lesson at this stage.

# UNIT 4

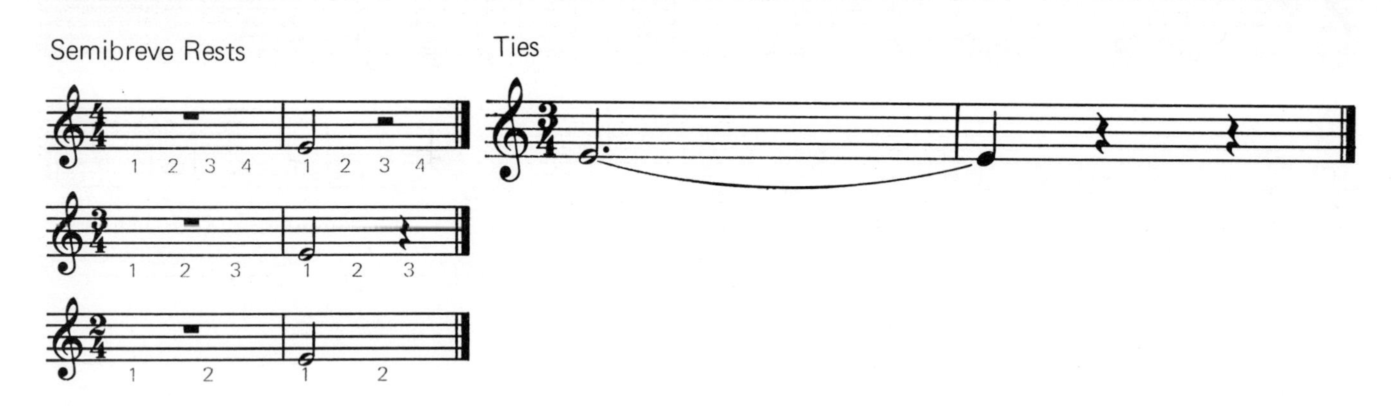


A semibreve rest is used to show any complete bar of rest, regardless of the number of beats in the bar. When it occurs you must examine the time-signature to find the number of beats to be counted. Compare the three examples.

A tie is a curved line placed over or under two notes of the same pitch. The tie joins the notes together making one continuous note. In order to produce one continuous note, the second note must not be tongued.

## MARCH

In a bright march tempo

Adapted from a melody by Derek Hyde

## Tone development

1. Play the exercise with the facial muscles firm and the corners of the lips tucked inwards.
2. Use the diaphragm to maintain an even air pressure.
3. Check the position of the bottom lip, feeling for a contact point that allows the reed to vibrate at its maximum efficiency.

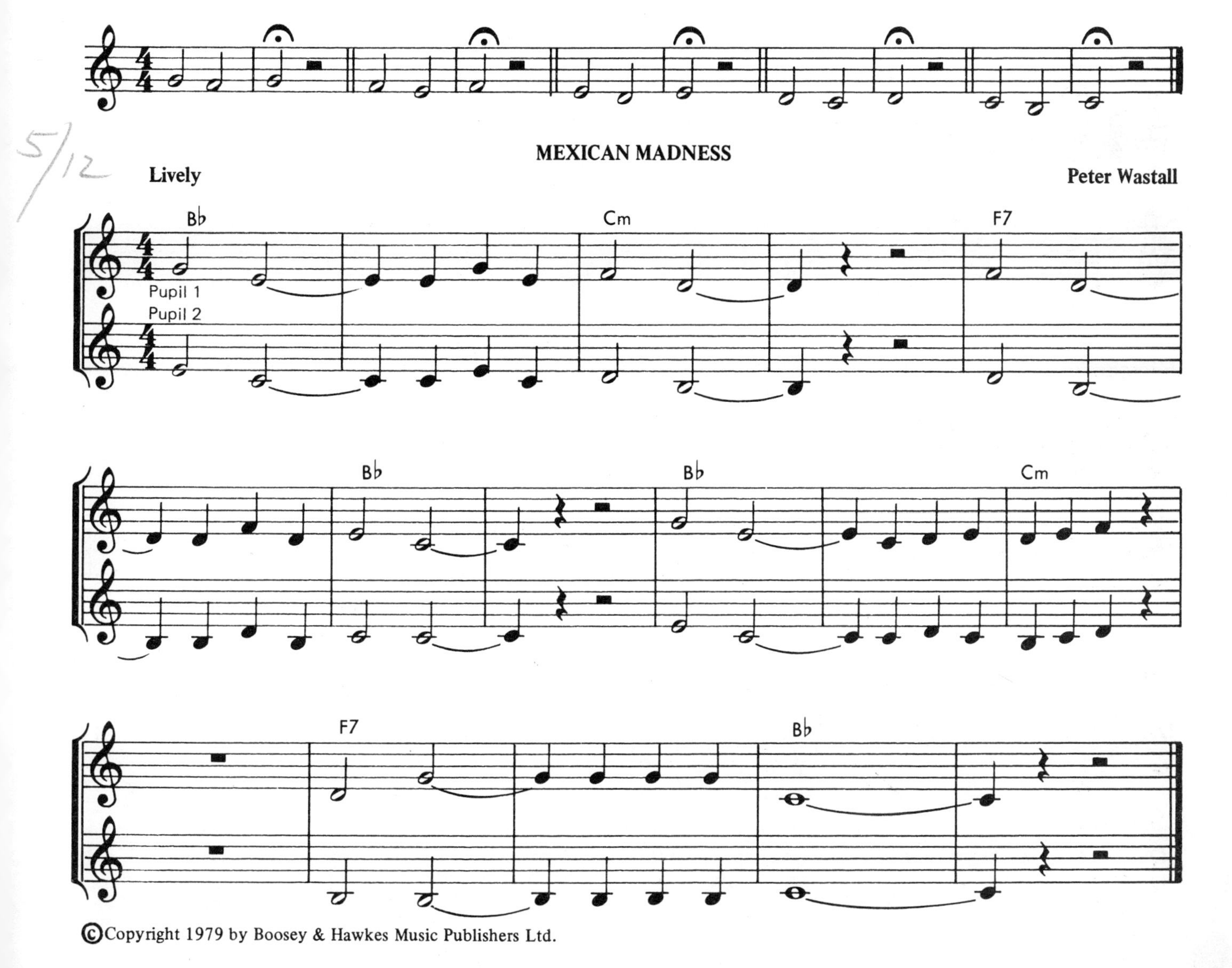

# UNIT 5

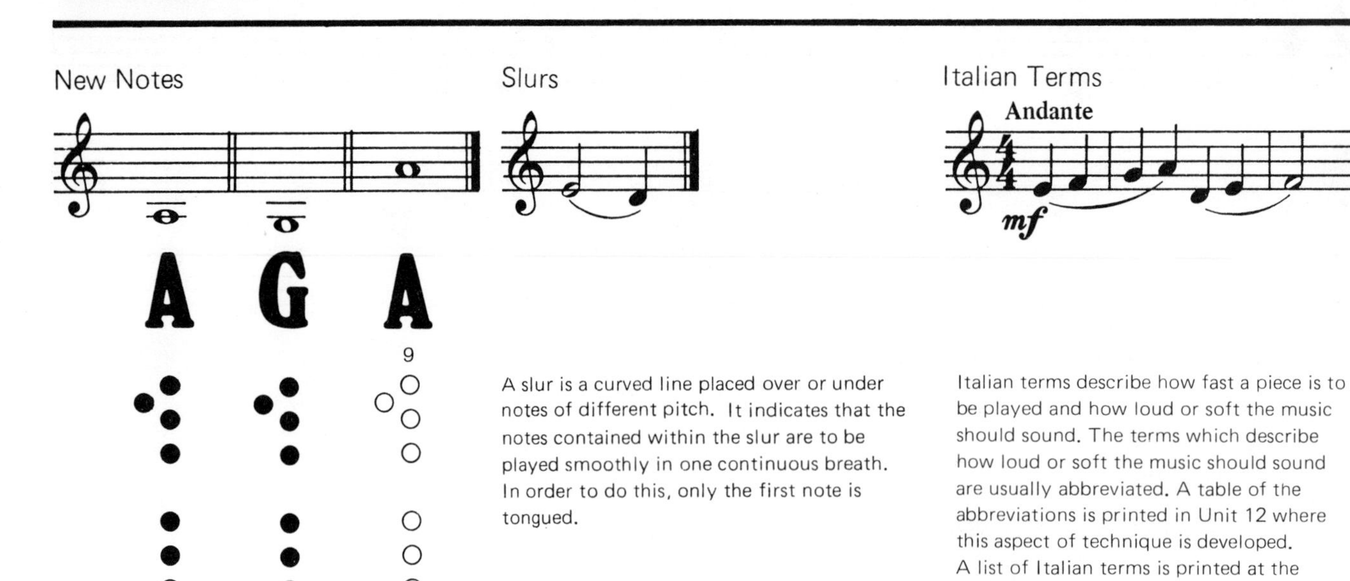


A slur is a curved line placed over or under notes of different pitch. It indicates that the notes contained within the slur are to be played smoothly in one continuous breath. In order to do this, only the first note is tongued.

Italian terms describe how fast a piece is to be played and how loud or soft the music should sound. The terms which describe how loud or soft the music should sound are usually abbreviated. A table of the abbreviations is printed in Unit 12 where this aspect of technique is developed. A list of Italian terms is printed at the end of the book.

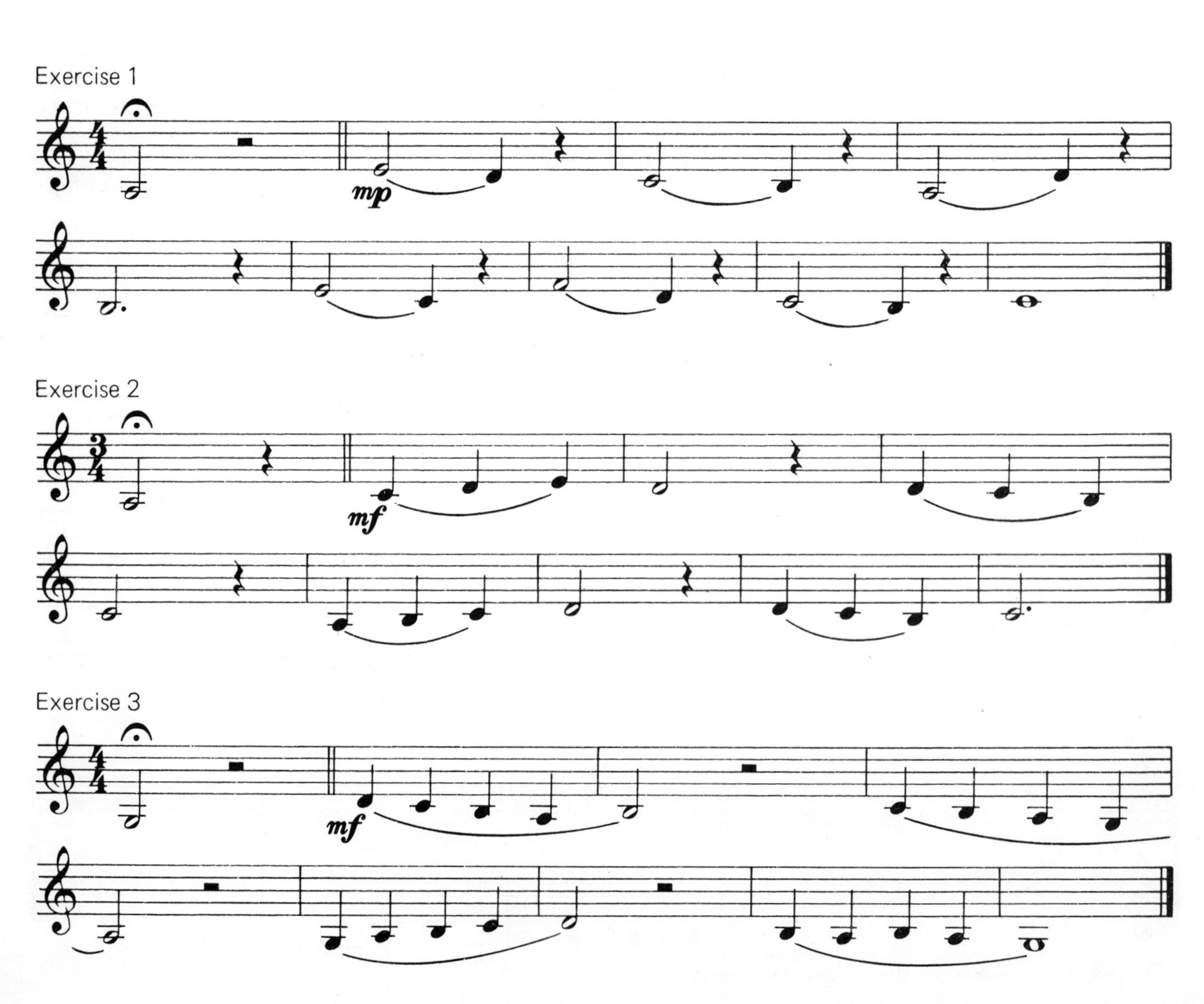

Exercise 4

## Finger technique

1. Play the first note of each exercise with the finger muscles firm and the left wrist somewhat relaxed.
2. When playing A, move to key 9 by pivoting the first finger; only the side of the top joint should touch the key.
3. On returning to the first note, ensure that the thumb and finger(s) touch down together.
4. Repeat exercise (a) using the notes shown in exercises (b) (c) and (d).

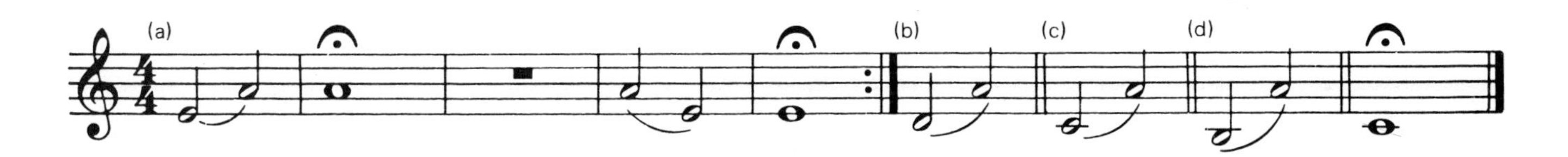

# UNIT 6

## Staccato Marks

When a dot is placed over or under a note it indicates that the note is to sound detached. To achieve this, the note is played shorter than its printed value, often producing a clipped effect, rather like saying the word TAP.

## Quavers

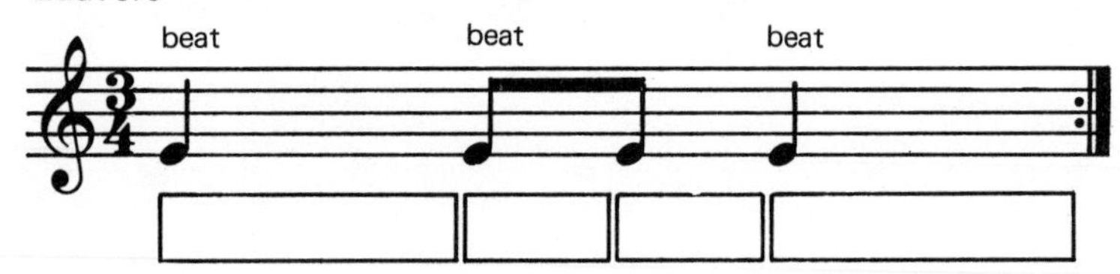


The value of a quaver is half a crotchet: it is printed with a tail on the end of its stem. For ease of reading, groups of quavers usually have their tails joined together.

Exercise 1

Exercise 2

Exercise 3

## Aids to music reading

When you play quavers read them like a two-syllable word. For example, when you read the word 'Doctor', you don't read 'Doc' then 'tor', you read 'Doctor'. This 'block' reading skill should be developed at the earliest possible stage of music reading. To help this development, each time quavers occur, make a conscious effort to read both notes at the same time.

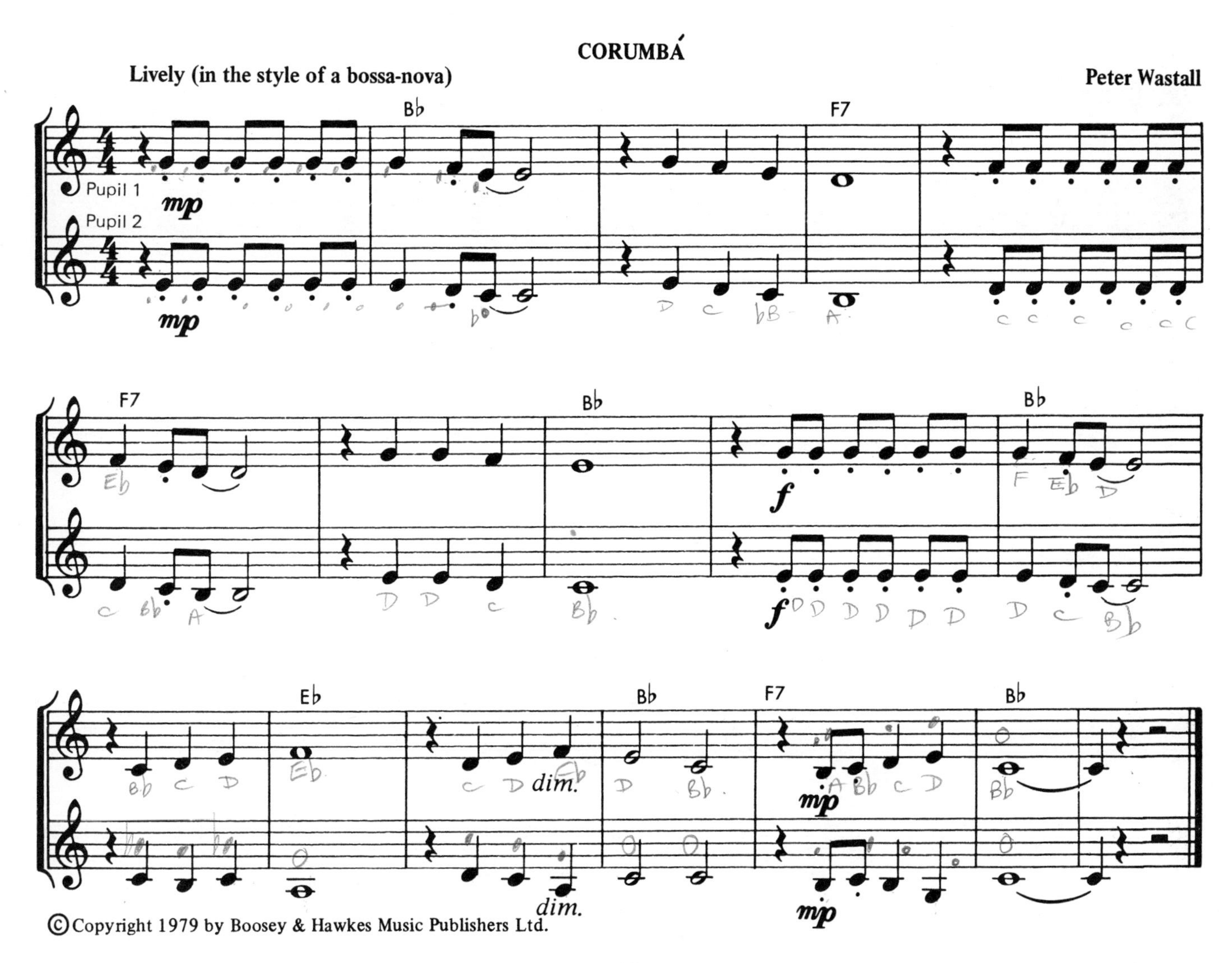

# UNIT 7

New Notes

B♭ B♭

Flat Signs

Every note in music can be raised or lowered half a tone. The sign for lowering a note half a tone is the flat sign shown in the example above. Compare the sound of low B♭ with the natural B used in units 3 - 6.

Accent Signs

An accent sign placed over or under a note means that the note must be given a strong attack with the tongue. Often this strong attack is combined with a little 'punch' from the diaphragm.

## A MELODY IN PHRYGIAN MODE

No. 28 from "Mikrokosmos" Vol. 1

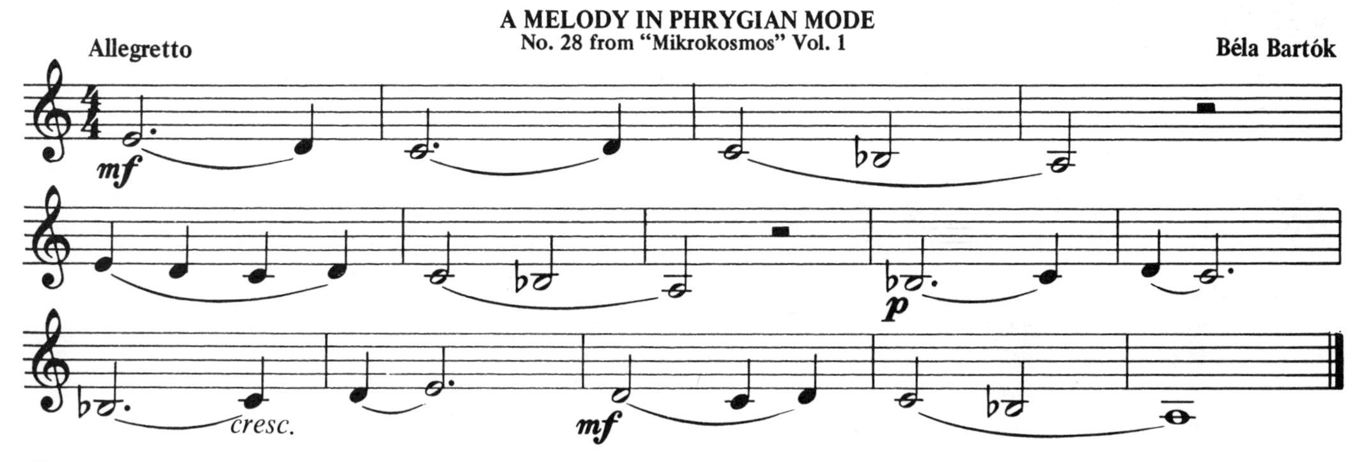




### Finger technique

1. When moving to B♭, use the side of the first finger for key 9 and the edge of the thumb for key 12, so that together they produce a type of pinching action.
2. When playing B♭, ensure that the thumb hole is completely open and the thumb ring raised; if necessary slightly bend the knuckle of the thumb.
3. Repeat exercise (a) using the notes shown in exercises (b) (c) (d) and (e).
4. On returning to the first note of exercises (b) (c) (d) and (e), listen for the thumb and finger(s) touching down together.

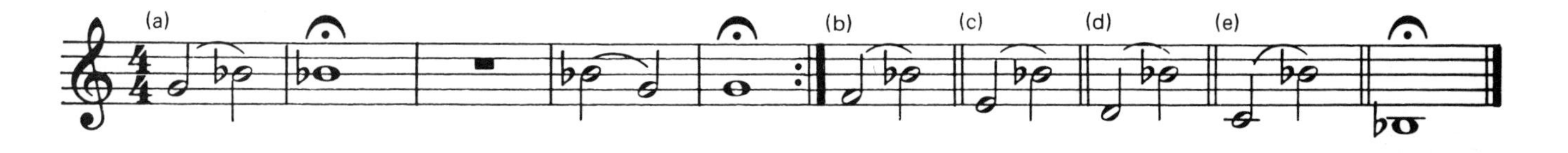


## GERMAN DANCE

## ELLACOMBE

# UNIT 8

## New Notes

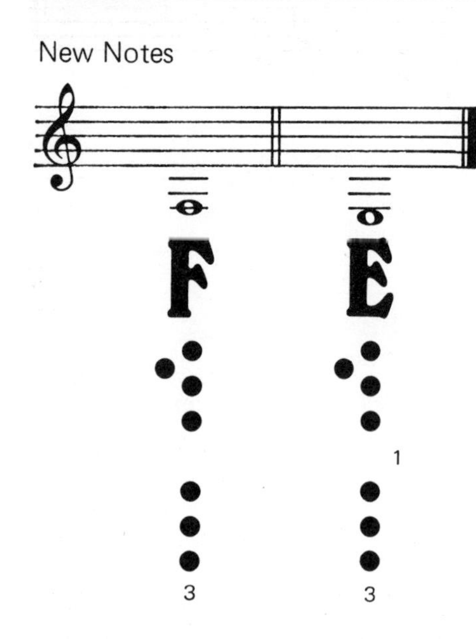


## Keys and Key-signatures

*Because of the key-signature, both these notes must be played as B♭.

When flat signs are placed at the beginning of each staff they are called a key-signature. Each flat is placed on a specific line or space indicating that every note with that letter name is to be played as if the flat were against the note. The two keys that use the key-signature with one flat are: F Major and D Minor

## Accidentals

*Because of the accidental, both these notes must be played as B♭.

When a flat or sharp is used that is not in the key-signature it is called an accidental. An accidental lasts until the next bar-line, and because of this, affects any subsequent note of the same pitch in that bar.

F Major

### Exercise 1

### Exercise 2

### Exercise 3

## Scales and arpeggios

F Major, to be played from memory

## Musicianship

Articulation (tonguing and slurring used in wind music) plays an important part in the creation of expression. It is the speech of music and can be thought of as the music equivalent of elocution. The tongue must be expressive, varying both the syllable formed and the strength of touch. In this unit concentrate on improving your articulation, using the pronunciation to give additional meaning to the phrases.

# CONCERT PIECES FOR UNITS 1-8

Piano accompaniments to the concert pieces are available in a separate accompaniment book. These should be used to provide experience in playing with an accompanist. 'Humming Song' by Schumann and 'Chorus' by Gluck are examples of music that have been set for early grade examinations.

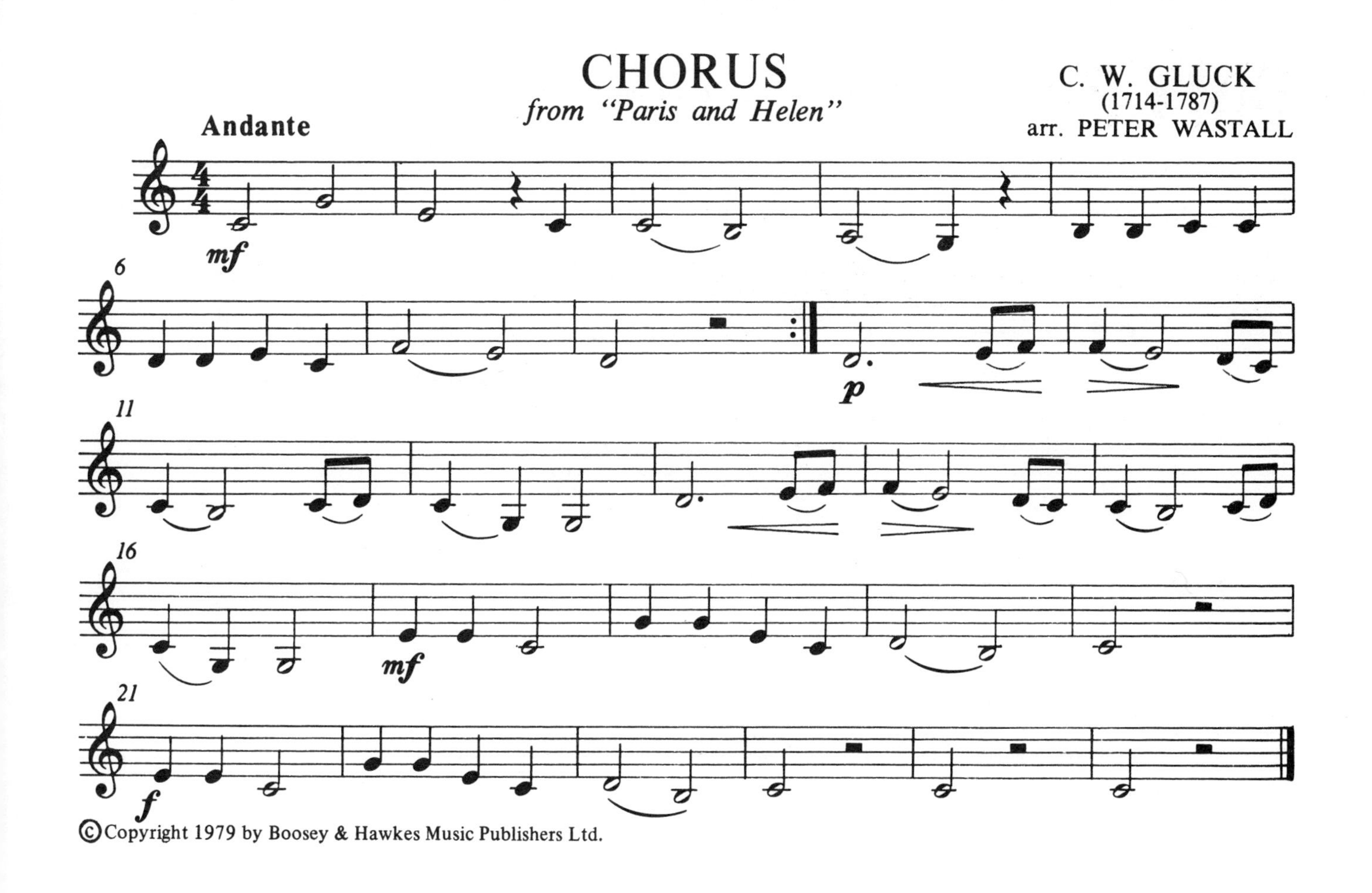
CHORUS
from "Paris and Helen"
C. W. GLUCK
(1714-1787)
arr. PETER WASTALL
Andante
mf
p
mf
f
©Copyright 1979 by Boosey & Hawkes Music Publishers Ltd.

HUMMING SONG
from "Album for the young" op. 68
ROBERT SCHUMANN
(1810-1856)
arr. PETER WASTALL
Not fast
p
p
©Copyright 1979 by Boosey & Hawkes Music Publishers Ltd.

# UNIT 9

## Keys and Key-signatures

The two keys that have no flats (or sharps) in their key-signatures are: C Major and A Minor. The music in this unit illustrates C Major.

## Dotted Crotchets

Since a dot after a note lengthens that note by half its value, the value of a dotted crotchet will be one and a half crotchet beats, the same length of sound as three quavers added together. Look at the example, then study the similarity of bars 2 and 3 in the first exercise.

C Major

Exercise 1

Exercise 2

Exercise 3

## The Upper Register

A complete range of new notes can be produced by adding key 12 to the fingerings already learned. The new notes are shown in unit 10, but the following exercise should be used as preparatory material. To achieve the maximum benefit, it should be memorised and practised away from the printed music. Once the exercise can be played satisfactorily, exercise 1 from unit 10 should also be memorised and used as additional preparatory material.

# UNIT 10

The Upper Register

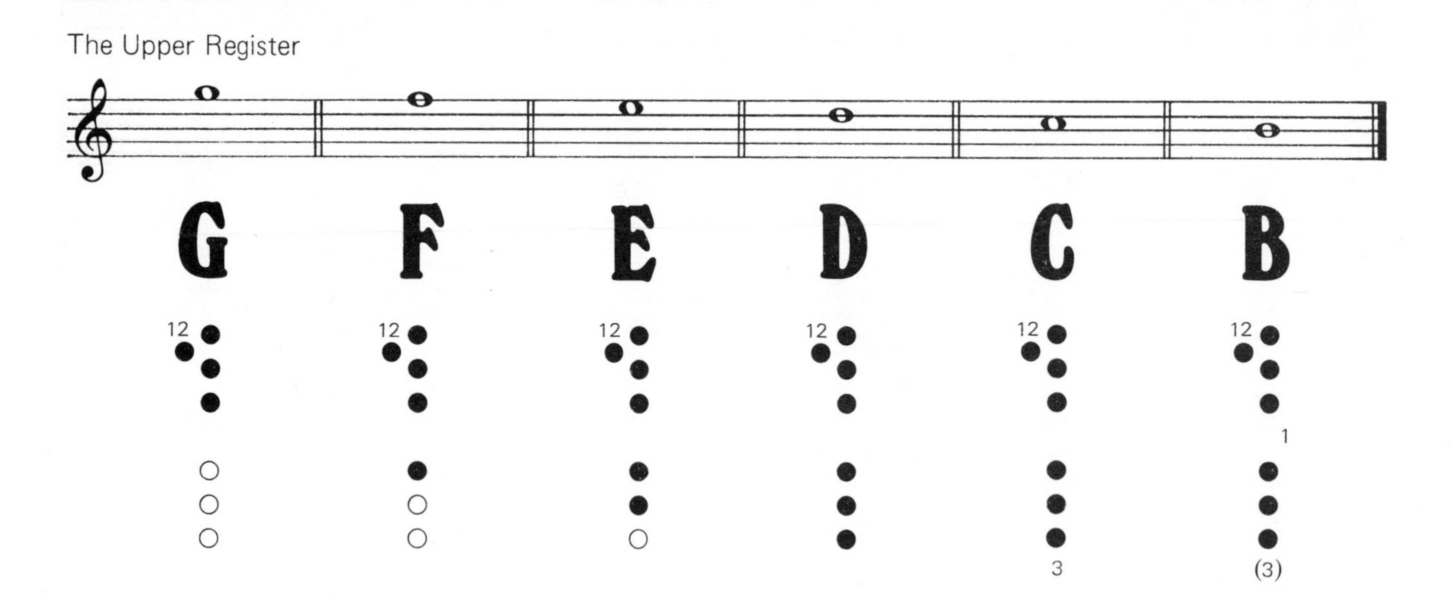


Exercise 1

Exercise 2

Exercise 3

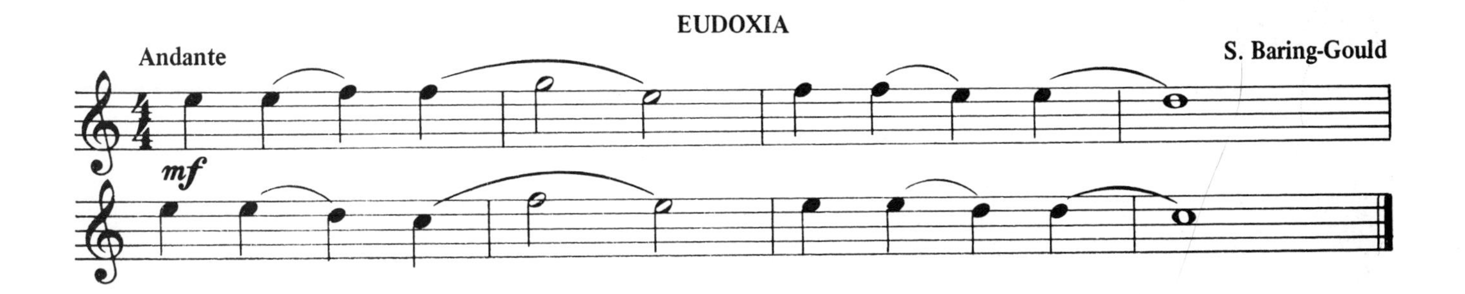


## Finger technique

1. Use the first note to establish a good finger and embouchure position.
2. In bar 3, do not release the right hand fingers when playing the low G. Use the right hand to keep the clarinet position stable.
3. When the left hand is released, move only a small distance from the holes, maintaining the basic hand and finger shape.
4. In bar 4, listen for the fingers and thumb touching down together.
5. Repeat exercise (a) using the notes shown in exercises (b) (c) (d) and (e).

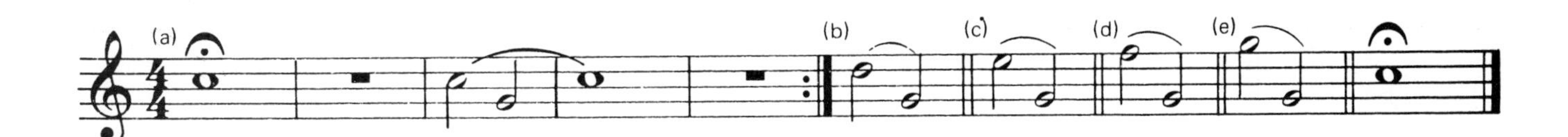


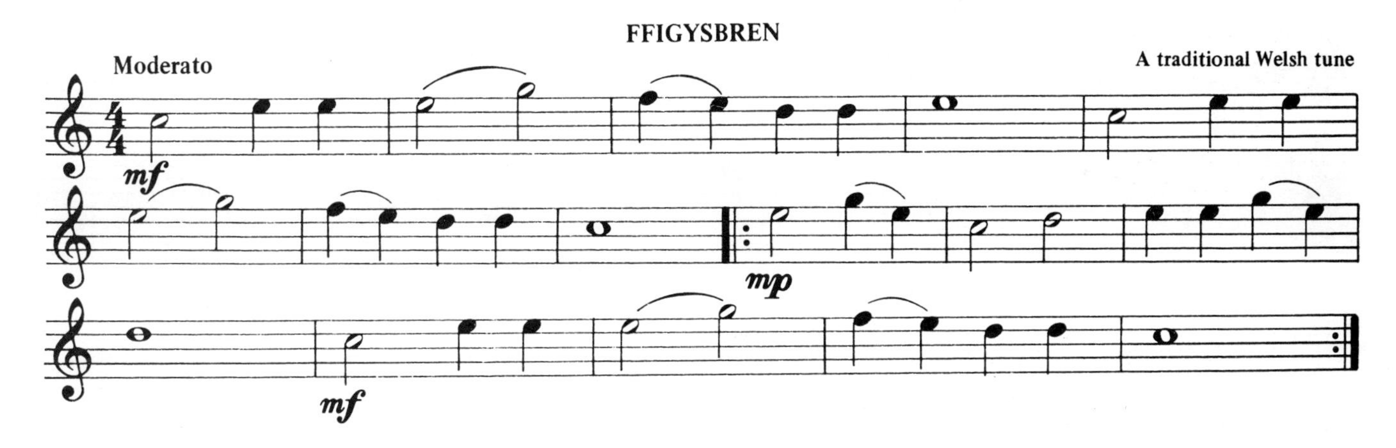


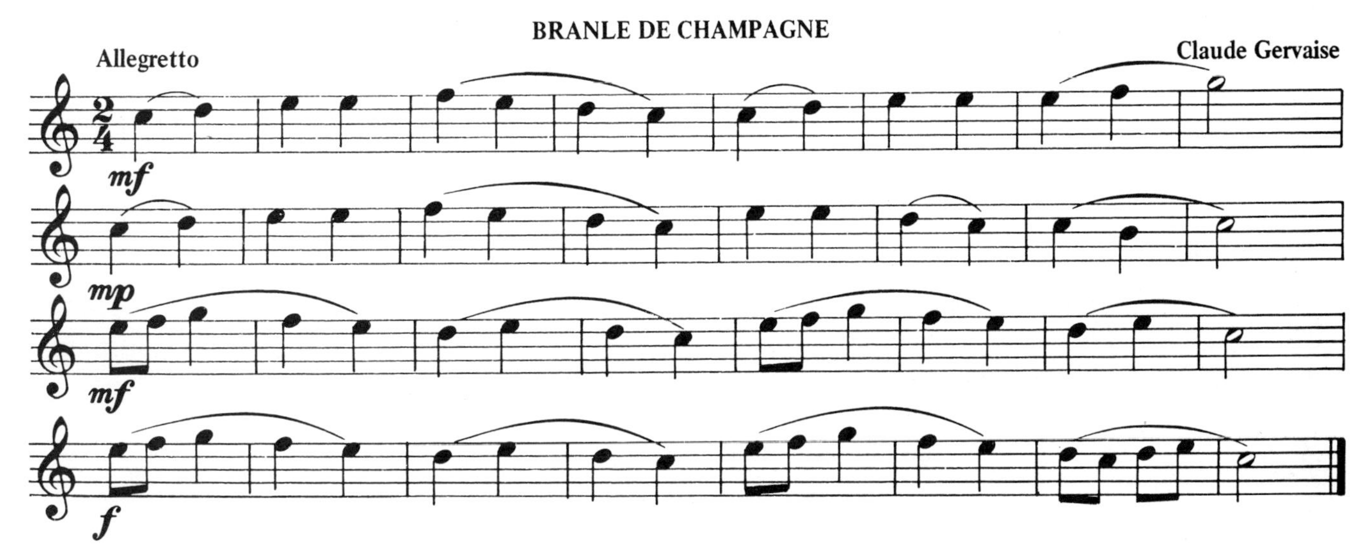

# UNIT 11

New Notes

Sharp Signs

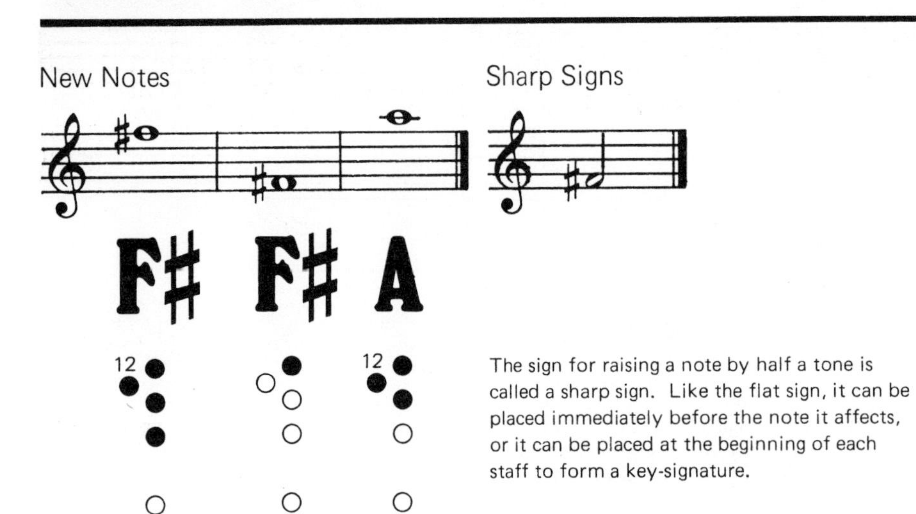


The sign for raising a note by half a tone is called a sharp sign. Like the flat sign, it can be placed immediately before the note it affects, or it can be placed at the beginning of each staff to form a key-signature.

A New Key-signature

*Because of the key-signature, both these notes must be played as F♯.

The two keys that use the key-signature with one sharp are: G Major and E Minor. The music in this unit illustrates G Major.

G Major

Exercise 1

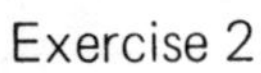

Exercise 2

Exercise 3

## Scales and arpeggios

G Major, to be played from memory.

## Finger technique

1. When moving from the upper register to key 9, use a pivoting action with the first finger. As in unit 5, it is the side of the top joint that should touch the key.
2. When moving from the upper register to either A or G, keep the right hand fingers down.
3. When playing lower register F♯ the right hand fingers must be raised.

# UNIT 12

## Natural Signs

A natural sign is used to cancel a flat or sharp. Since it is a type of accidental, it will only last for the bar in which it is printed. However, if a note that has been altered occurs again in the next bar, an additional accidental is often used to confirm that the note has returned to its original pitch.

## Italian Terms

| | | | |
|---|---|---|---|
| ***pp*** | very soft | ***ff*** | very loud |
| ***p*** | soft | ***f*** | loud |
| ***mp*** | moderately soft | ***mf*** | moderately loud |
| (decrescendo hairpin) | gradually softer | (crescendo hairpin) | gradually louder |

Italian terms also describe the mood of a piece, changes of mood and large repeats such as da capo. As with Italian terms introduced earlier, English translations can be found at the end of the book.

A table of Italian terms which show how loud or soft the music should sound is printed above. It should be used in conjunction with the tuning technique introduced in this unit.

## Musicianship

Crescendos and diminuendos play an important part in creating expression but need careful use since they also have an effect on tuning. Basically, a crescendo (produced by increasing the air pressure) will make a note go sharp; and a diminuendo (produced by reducing the air pressure) will make a note go flat.

To stabilise the tuning, increase the bottom lip support during diminuendo, and decrease it during a crescendo.

# UNIT 13

New Notes

Quaver Rests

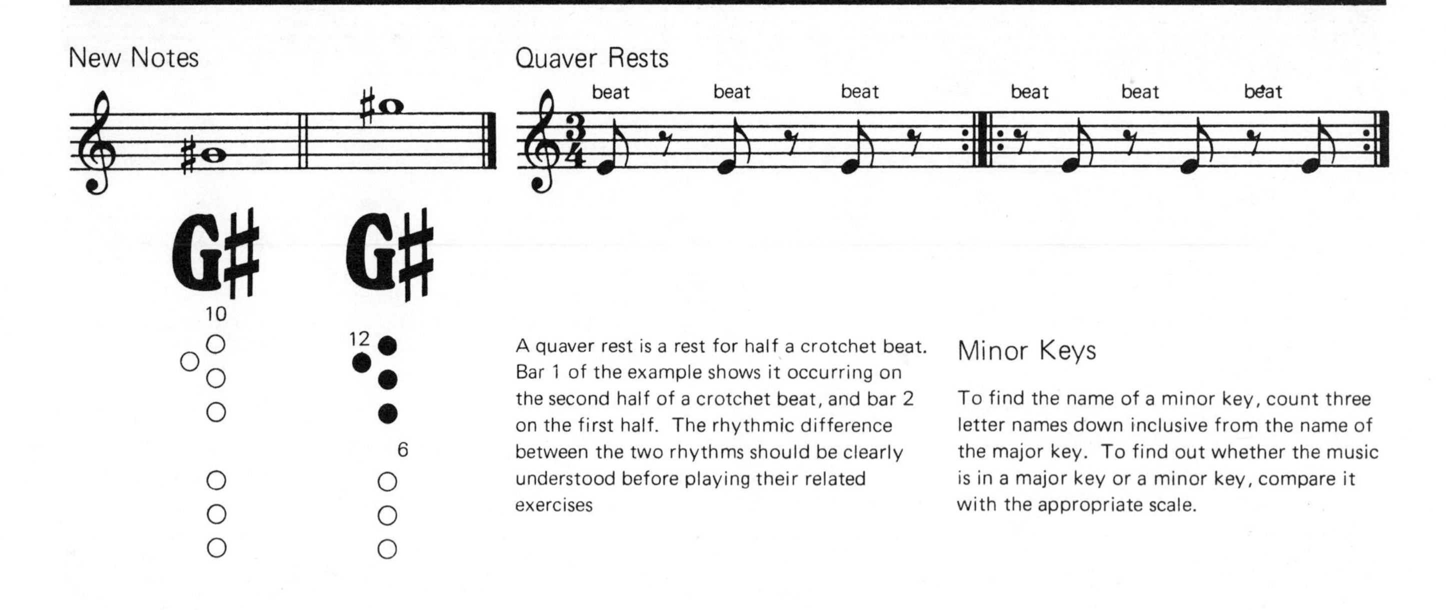


A quaver rest is a rest for half a crotchet beat. Bar 1 of the example shows it occurring on the second half of a crotchet beat, and bar 2 on the first half. The rhythmic difference between the two rhythms should be clearly understood before playing their related exercises

## Minor Keys

To find the name of a minor key, count three letter names down inclusive from the name of the major key. To find out whether the music is in a major key or a minor key, compare it with the appropriate scale.

## A Minor

Exercise 1

Exercise 2

## Scales and arpeggios

A Minor (harmonic form) to be played from memory.

## Scales and arpeggios

C Major, to be played from memory

## Finger technique

1. Play both exercises with the first finger muscles reasonably firm and the left wrist somewhat relaxed.
2. When moving to G♯, use a pivoting action similar to that developed for playing the note A.
3. Throughout both exercises, be careful not to destroy the basic hand position.

# UNIT 14

## Compound Time

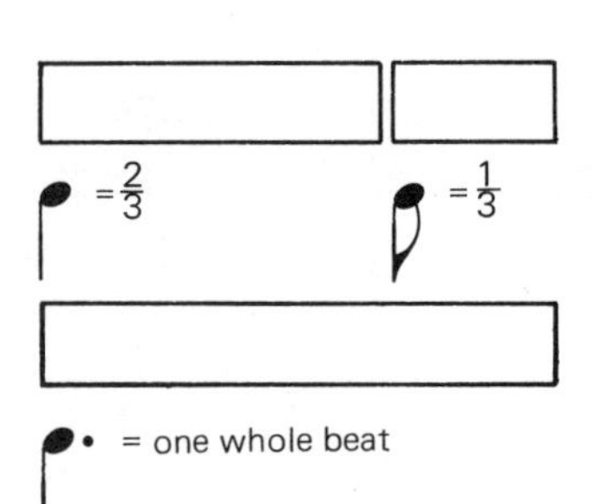

= one whole beat

## Compound Time-signatures

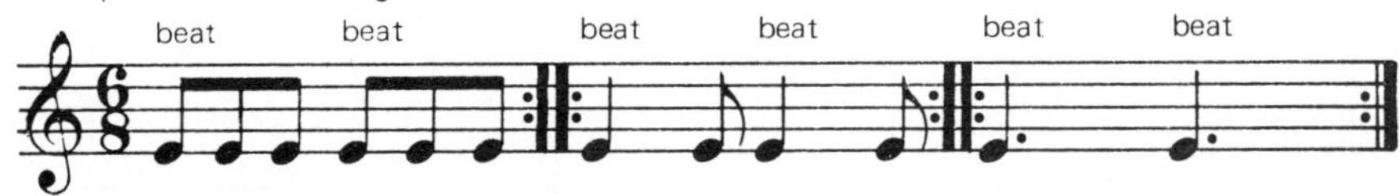


When the natural pulse of a piece divides itself into thirds of a beat, the music is said to be in compound time. The various notes retain the same value in relation to each other; for instance there are still two quavers in a crotchet, but their value in relation to the beat is changed to the values shown in the example.

To show the new note values a new set of time-signatures is used. The example shows six-eight, indicating two dotted crotchet beats in a bar. A chart showing the complete range of compound time-signatures and how they are applied is printed at the end of the book.

Exercise 1

Exercise 2

Exercise 3

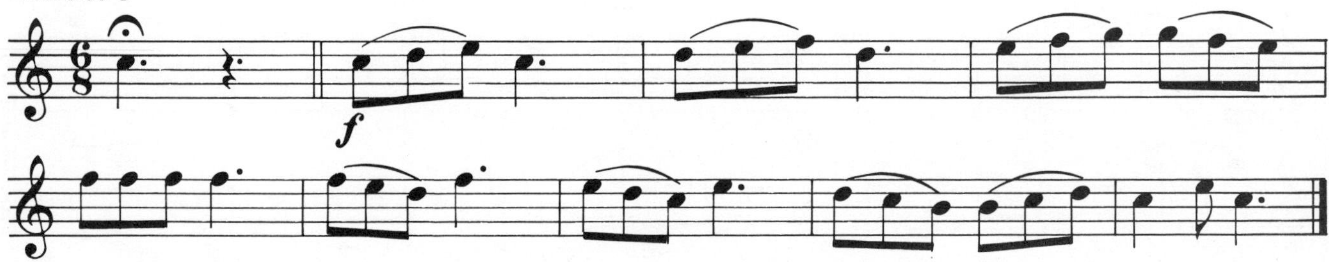

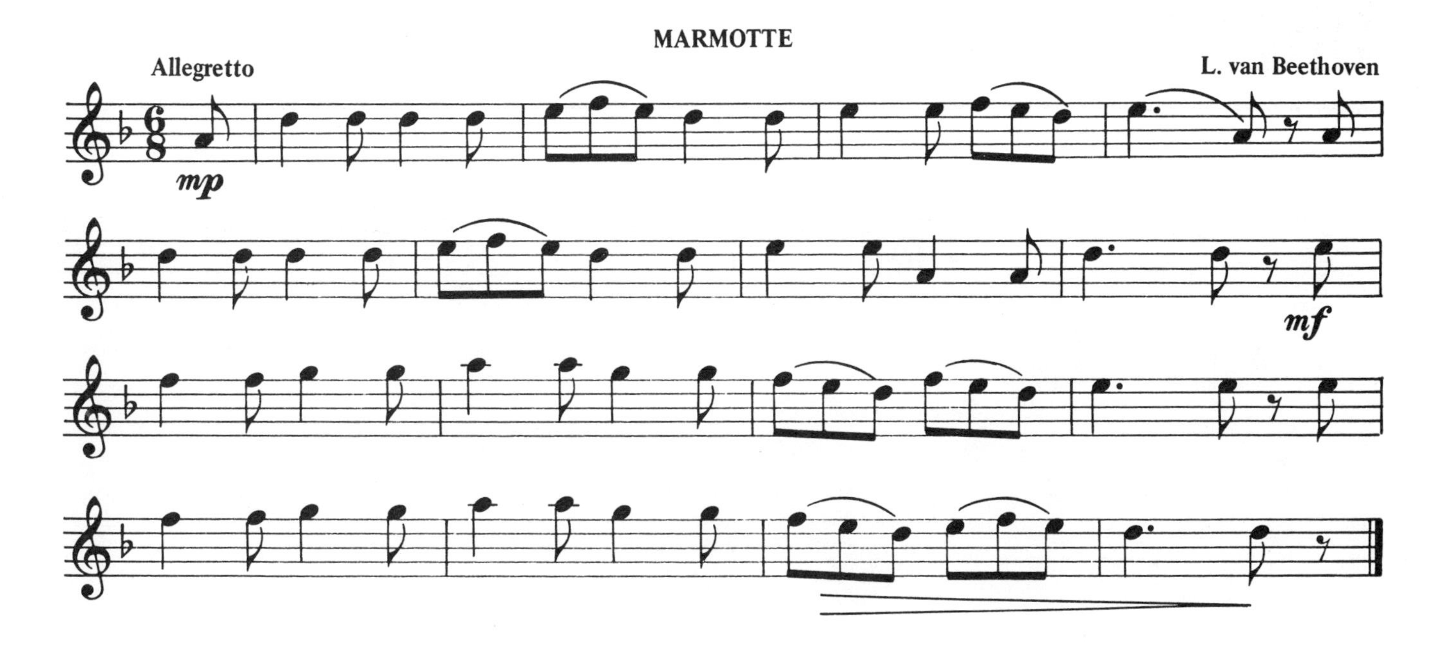


## Aids to music reading

When reading notes which are thirds of a beat, read them as if they were three-syllable words. As an example of this, try the first exercise thinking the word TENTATIVE as you play each group. When playing the pieces, apply this reading principle to all rhythmic groups contained within one beat.

# UNIT 15

New Notes

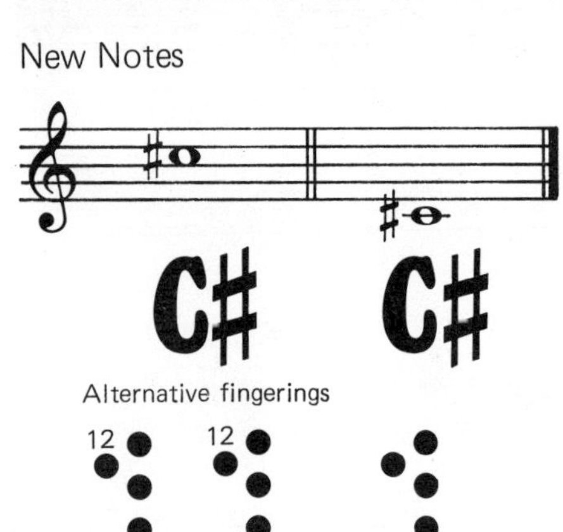


A New Key-signature

In sharp keys, the name of the major key can be found by counting one letter name up from the last sharp. The example shows a key-signature with two sharps, and since the last sharp is C♯, the name of the major key must be D Major.

Grace Notes

In their simplest form, grace notes are notes added to a melody to make the music sound more decorative. To show how they are used, first play the example without the pair of grace notes, then again, using the grace notes to decorate the B. As a general rule, grace notes should be played gracefully and lightly.

D Major

Exercise 1

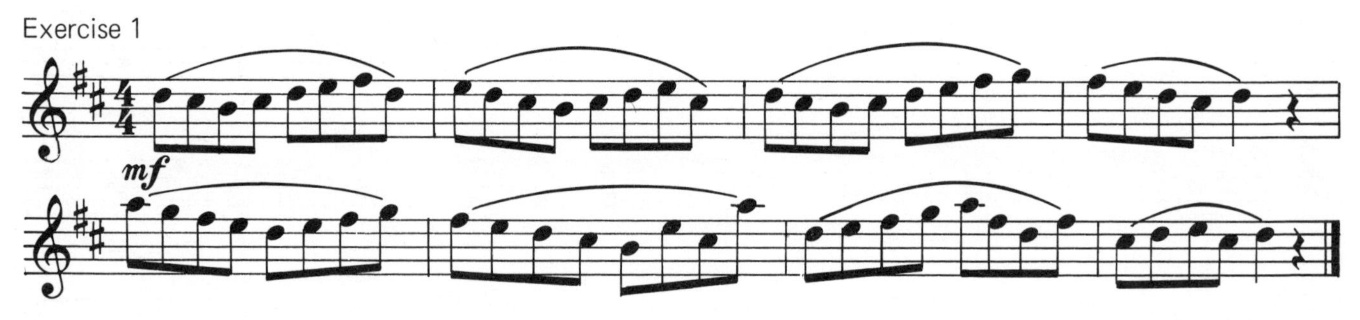

Exercise 2

Exercise 3

## Scales and arpeggios

D Major  to be played from memory

## Finger technique

1. Upper register C♯ can be fingered with key 2 or key 2a, and in many pieces either fingering is possible. However, it is usual to take the right hand fingering when the note occurs as an accidental (Brahms' 'Waltz', bar 7), or is part of a passage in D Major (exercise 1).

2. When upper register C♯ occurs in a chromatic passage (i.e. C♮ followed by C♯) key 2a must be used. To identify passages where this left hand fingering is needed it is customary to mark the note with the letter (L).

# UNIT 16

Tenuto Signs

1st and 2nd time bars

A tenuto sign placed over or under a note means that the note is to be played with a lingering pressure. Usually it is also associated with a type of tonguing where one syllable is added to another without any noticeable break in the air stream.

Sometimes the ending of a repeated section is altered the second time through. When this occurs, 1st and 2nd time bars are used. The example is taken from "Ein' feste Burg", in which bars 1 - 4 are played quite normally the first time through, but when they are repeated the first time bar is omitted and the second time bar played instead.

Exercise 1

Exercise 2

Exercise 3

## Musicianship

Sometimes the general character of a piece suggests that many of the notes should be played staccato. When this occurs, the dots on top of the notes are often omitted, leaving it to the instrumentalist to interpret the music in a staccato style. The "Duo" by Frédéric Berr is an example of this.

# CONCERT PIECES FOR UNITS 9 - 16

As with earlier concert pieces, piano accompaniments should be used to provide experience in playing with an accompanist. During the preparation of the pieces a start can be made on the grade 2 aural tests.

## AN OLD TALE

*from "24 Easy Pieces for Violin and Piano"*

ISTVÁN SZELÉNYI
(1904-1972)

## GERMAN DANCE

*from "12 German Dances"*

JOSEPH HAYDN
(1732-1809)
arr. PETER WASTALL

# MIDNIGHT IN TOBAGO

# UNIT 17

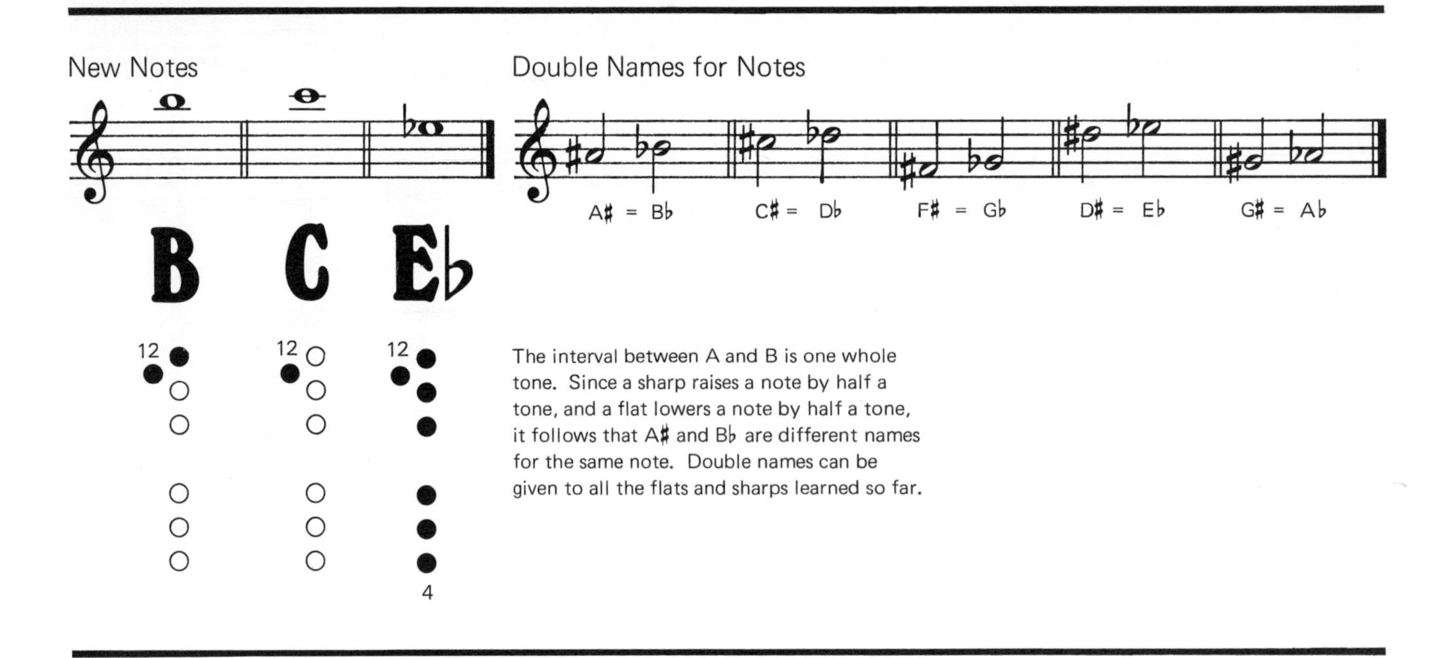


The interval between A and B is one whole tone. Since a sharp raises a note by half a tone, and a flat lowers a note by half a tone, it follows that A♯ and B♭ are different names for the same note. Double names can be given to all the flats and sharps learned so far.

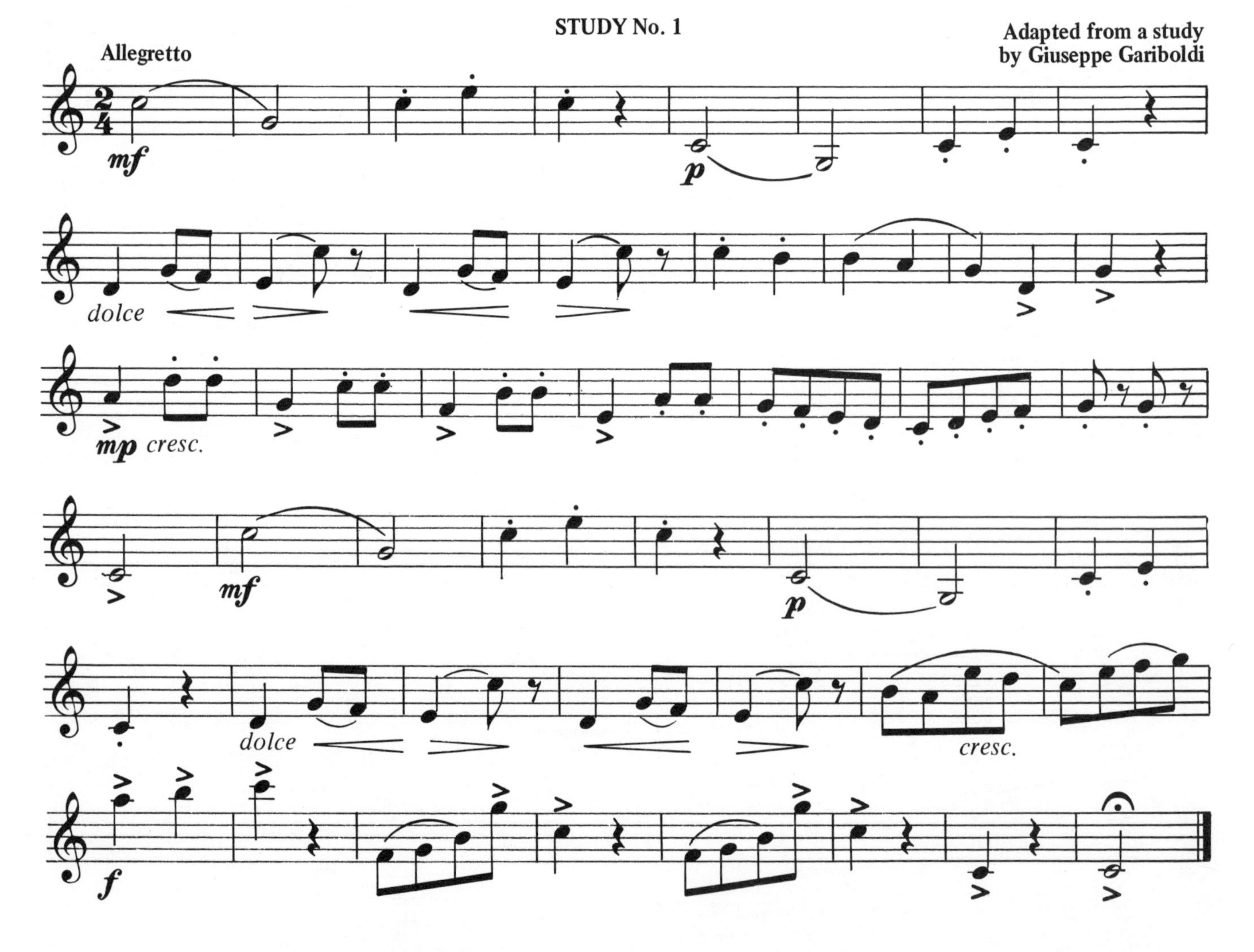

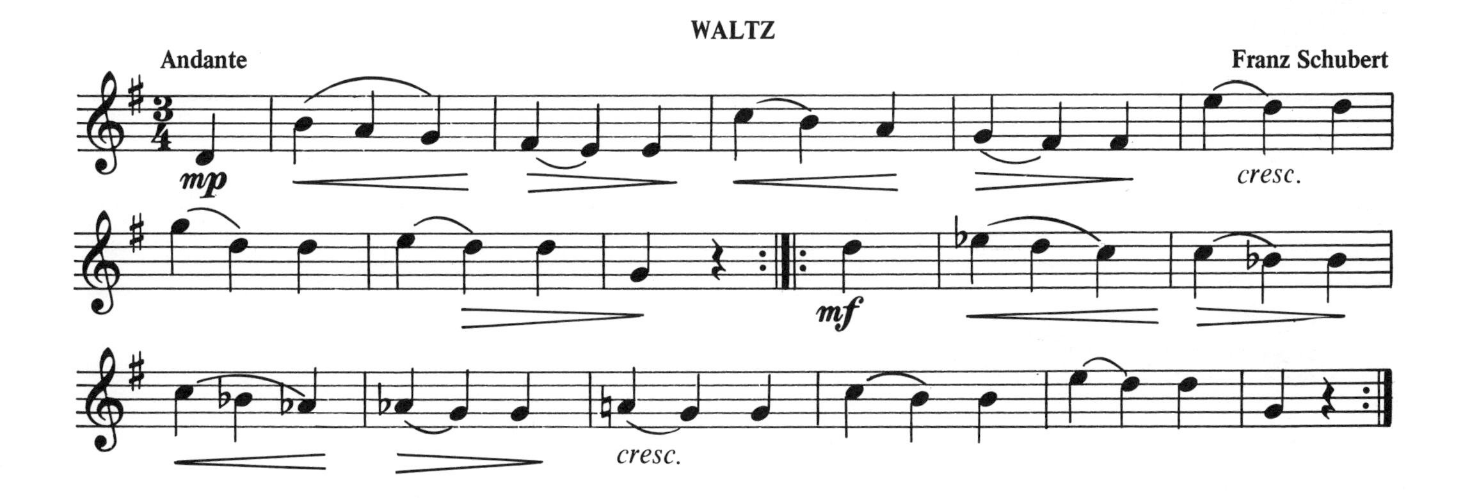


Finger technique

1. Key 3a is the left hand fingering for upper register C and low F♮. In the upper register, it is used when C is followed or preceded by E♭. Exercise (a) demonstrates this finger pattern.
2. When the left hand fingering for C is followed or preceded by B♮, the right hand fingering for B♮ (key 1a) must be used. This is demonstrated in exercise (b).

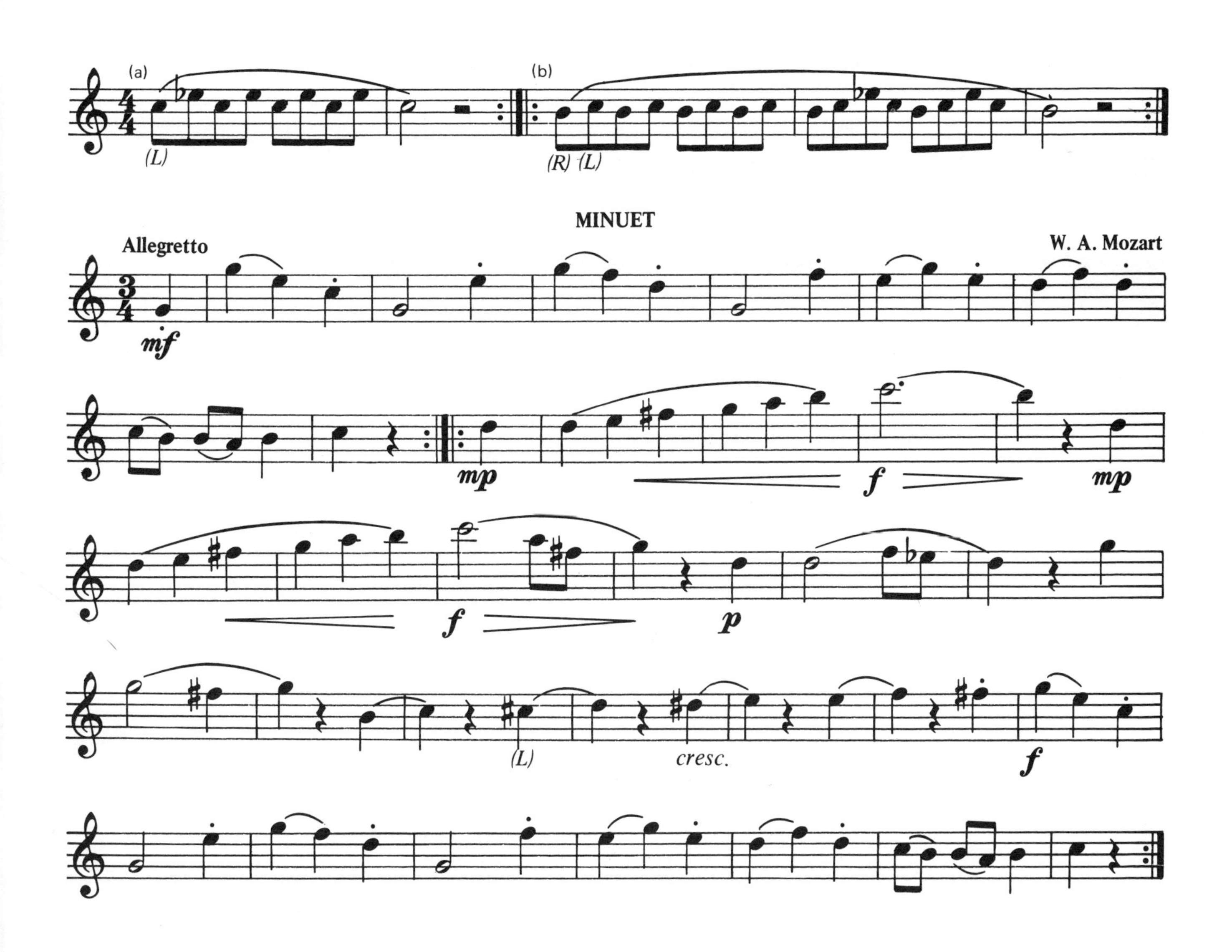

# UNIT 18

Semiquavers

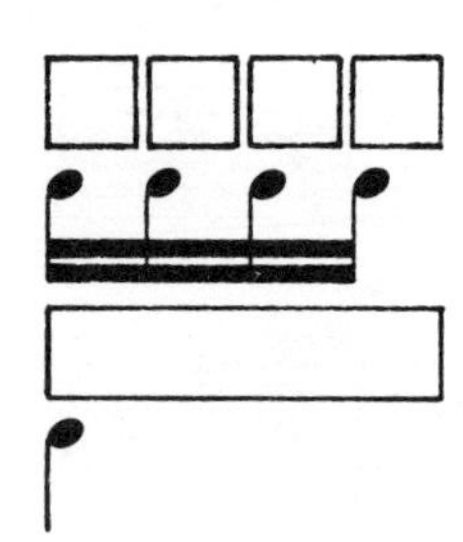

Syncopation

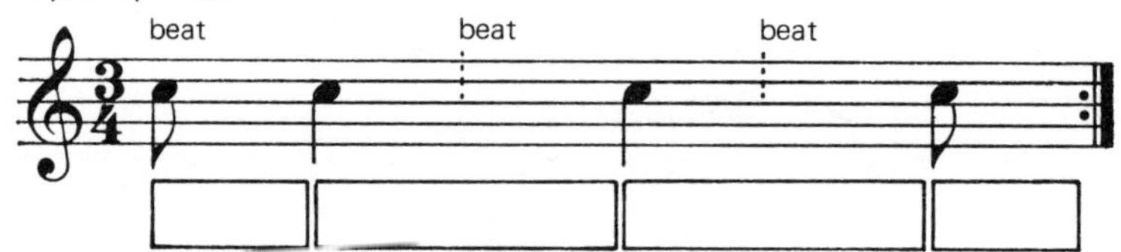


The value of a semiquaver is a quarter of a crotchet; it is printed with two tails on the end of its stem. As with quavers all the tails contained in one beat can be joined together.

A new rhythm, called syncopation, is produced when strongly accented notes occur between the beats instead of coinciding with them.

As shown in the duet, the surrounding quavers are usually played staccato to help bounce the syncopated notes off the beat.

Exercise 1

Exercise 2

Scales and arpeggios

F Major (two octaves) to be played from memory.

## Aids to music reading

With blocks of four semiquavers, read each group as you would a four-syllable word. Start with passages that are easy to finger (such as the two exercises shown opposite) and make a conscious effort to read each block of four semiquavers as a single unit.

# UNIT 19

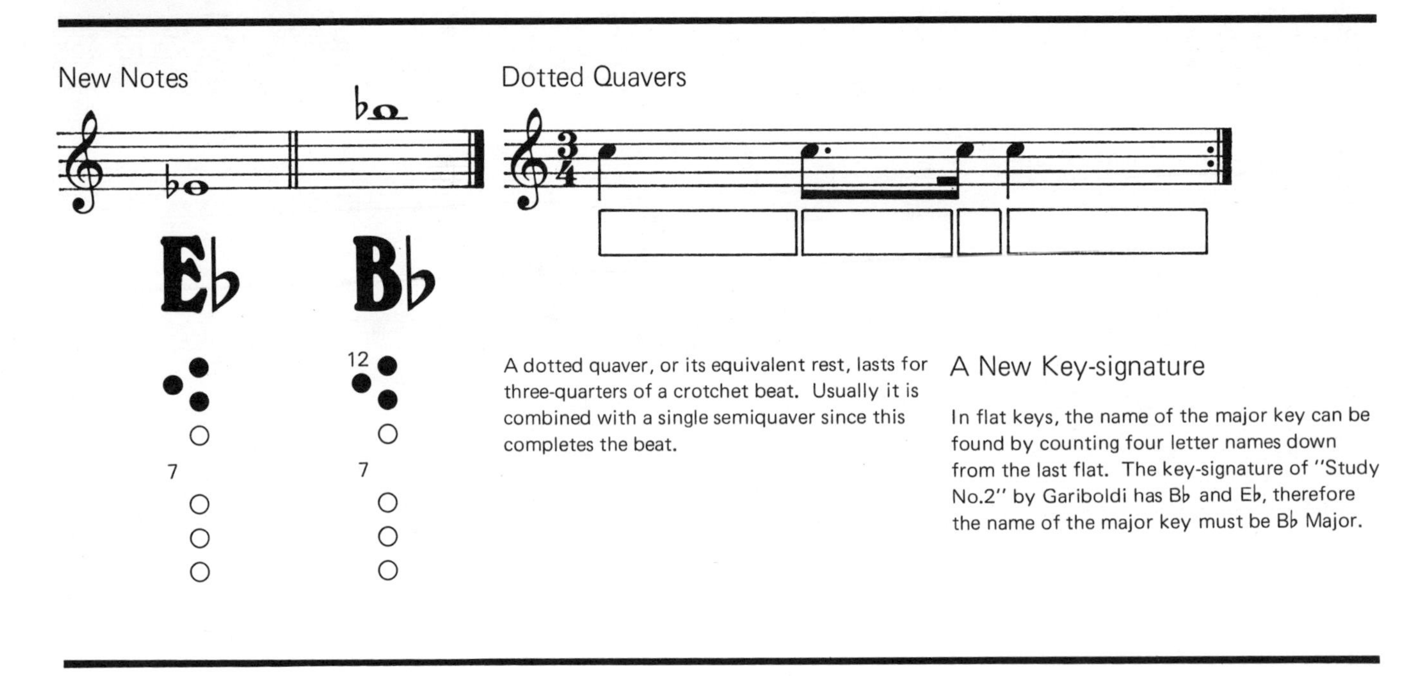


A dotted quaver, or its equivalent rest, lasts for three-quarters of a crotchet beat. Usually it is combined with a single semiquaver since this completes the beat.

## A New Key-signature

In flat keys, the name of the major key can be found by counting four letter names down from the last flat. The key-signature of "Study No.2" by Gariboldi has B♭ and E♭, therefore the name of the major key must be B♭ Major.

## Aids to music reading

The reading technique for a single semiquaver is to group the semiquaver with the note which follows. In lively movements a useful way to achieve this is to pronounce the two notes as if saying the word TODAY. As an example, play the first note of the "Soldier's March" by Schumann, then think TODAY. as you play the next two notes. This reading technique can be used every time a dotted rhythm occurs.

# UNIT 20

## Semiquaver Rests

A semiquaver rest is a rest for a quarter of a crotchet beat. Notice that it is similar to the semiquaver note, being printed with two tails. An example of the semiquaver rest can be found in the duet.

## Note patterns using Semiquavers

By combining semiquavers with quavers, several new rhythm patterns can be formed. The above examples should be studied carefully before playing the exercises.

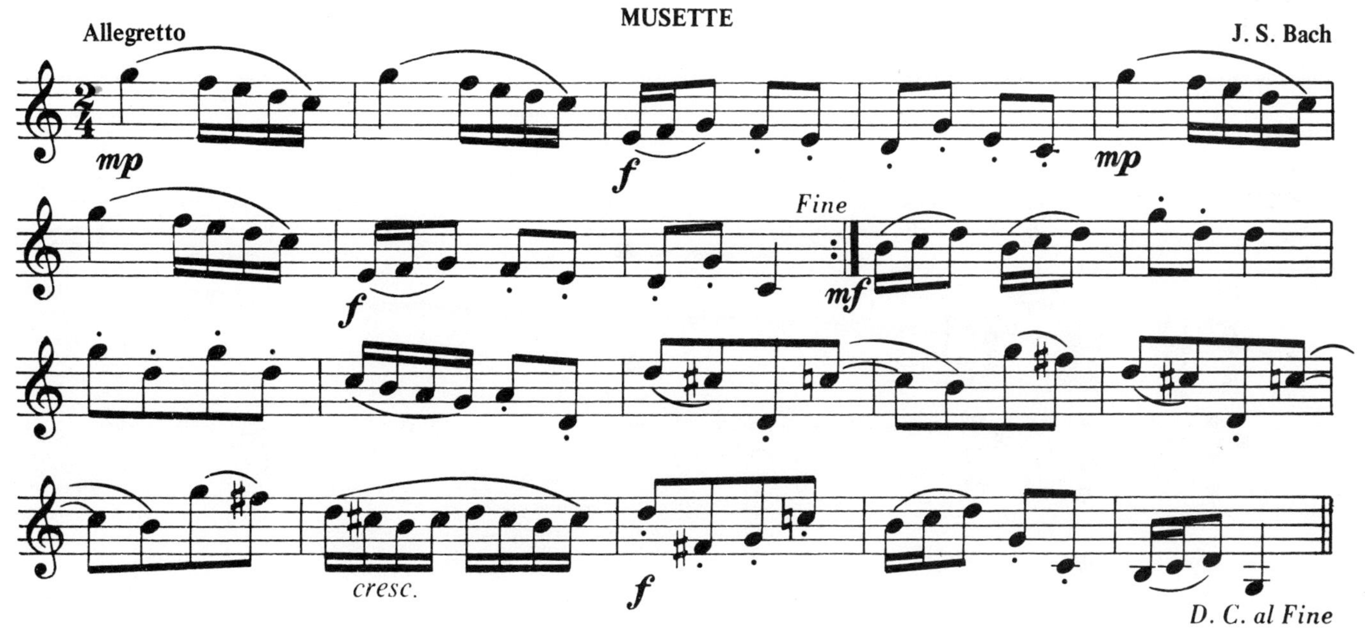


## Musicianship

As you play the "Duo" by Frédéric Berr, notice that the general character is one of smoothness. To achieve this smoothness, use a very gentle type of tonguing; rather like pronouncing the syllable DAH. When playing in this manner, we say we are interpreting the music in a legato style. Compare the style with that needed for playing the Bach "Musette", where the mood demands that many of the quavers be played with a crisp, neat staccato.

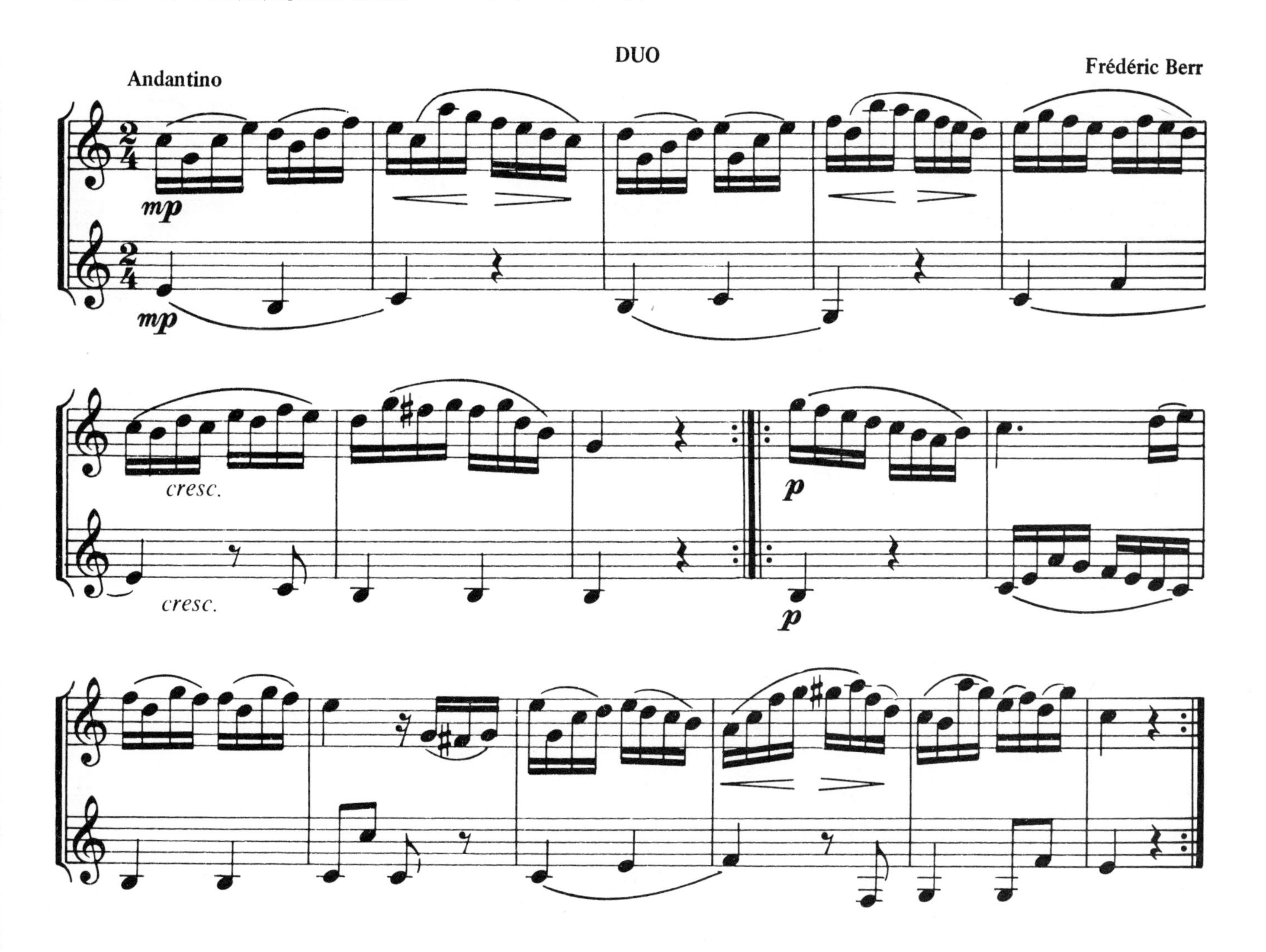

# UNIT 21

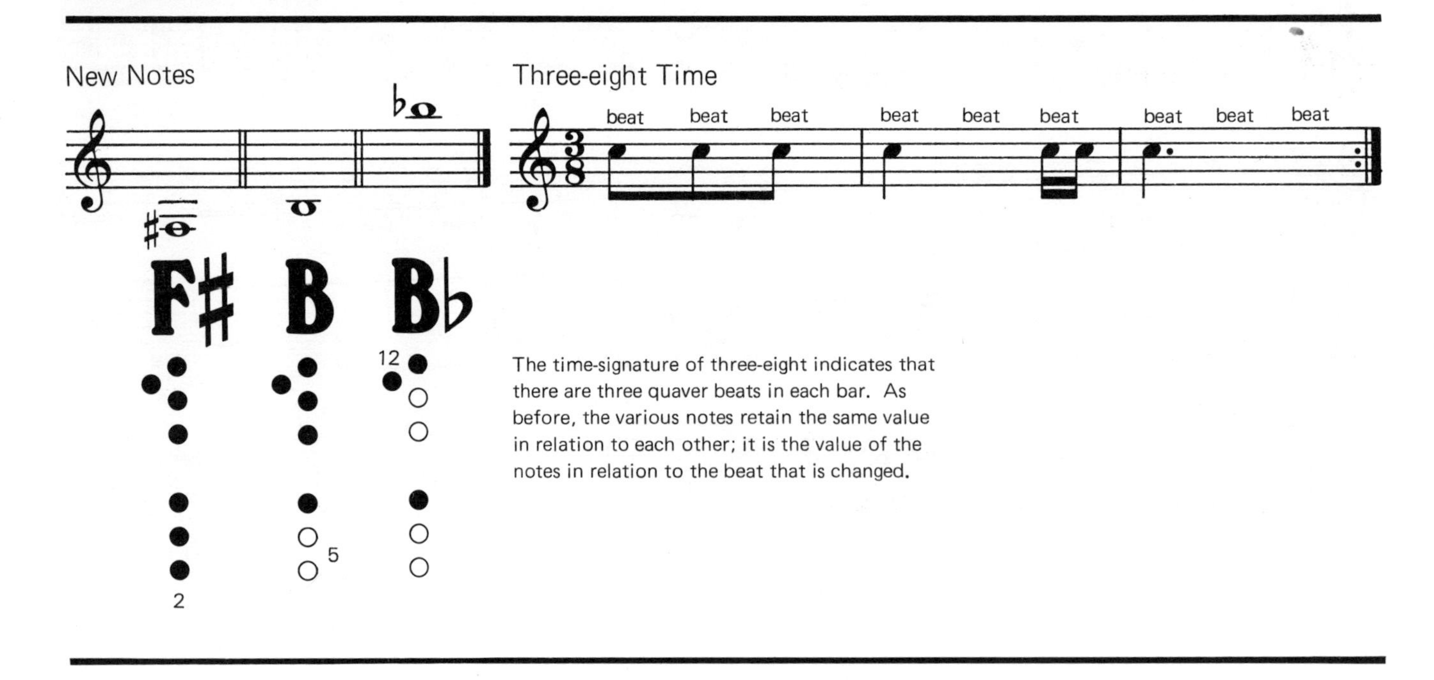


The time-signature of three-eight indicates that there are three quaver beats in each bar. As before, the various notes retain the same value in relation to each other; it is the value of the notes in relation to the beat that is changed.

## AYLESFORD'S PIECE

## Finger technique

1. When lower register B♮ occurs in a chromatic passage (Aylesford's Piece, bars 1 and 2), the fingering shown in this unit is the one that must be used. In the upper register, this chromatic fingering will apply to F♯ (unit 22).

2. When upper register B♭ is followed or preceded by notes using the right hand, the alternative fingering shown in this unit is often used. Examples, identified with the letter (X), can be found in "Hunting Song" by Schumann.

## HUNTING SONG

# UNIT 22

## Acciaccaturas

An acciaccatura is a small grace note with a stroke through its stem. It should be played on the beat and as short as possible.

## Changes of Time-signature

Sometimes a time-signature is changed during the course of a piece. When this occurs the speed of the beat usually remains the same; it is the pulse pattern that changes. The example is taken from "Hymn to Nature" by István Szelényi.

## HYMN TO NATURE

from "24 Easy Pieces for Violin & Piano"

Istvan Szelényi (1904–1972)

Finger technique

1. When lower register A occurs as an acciaccatura to G, the trill fingering for A (key 9a) is often used. An example occurs in bar 2 of the study by Wilhelm Popp.
2. When upper register B occurs as an acciaccatura to A, the trill fingering for B (A plus key 11) should be used. An example occurs in bar 4 of the study by Wilhelm Popp.

## MINUET

W. A. Mozart

# UNIT 23

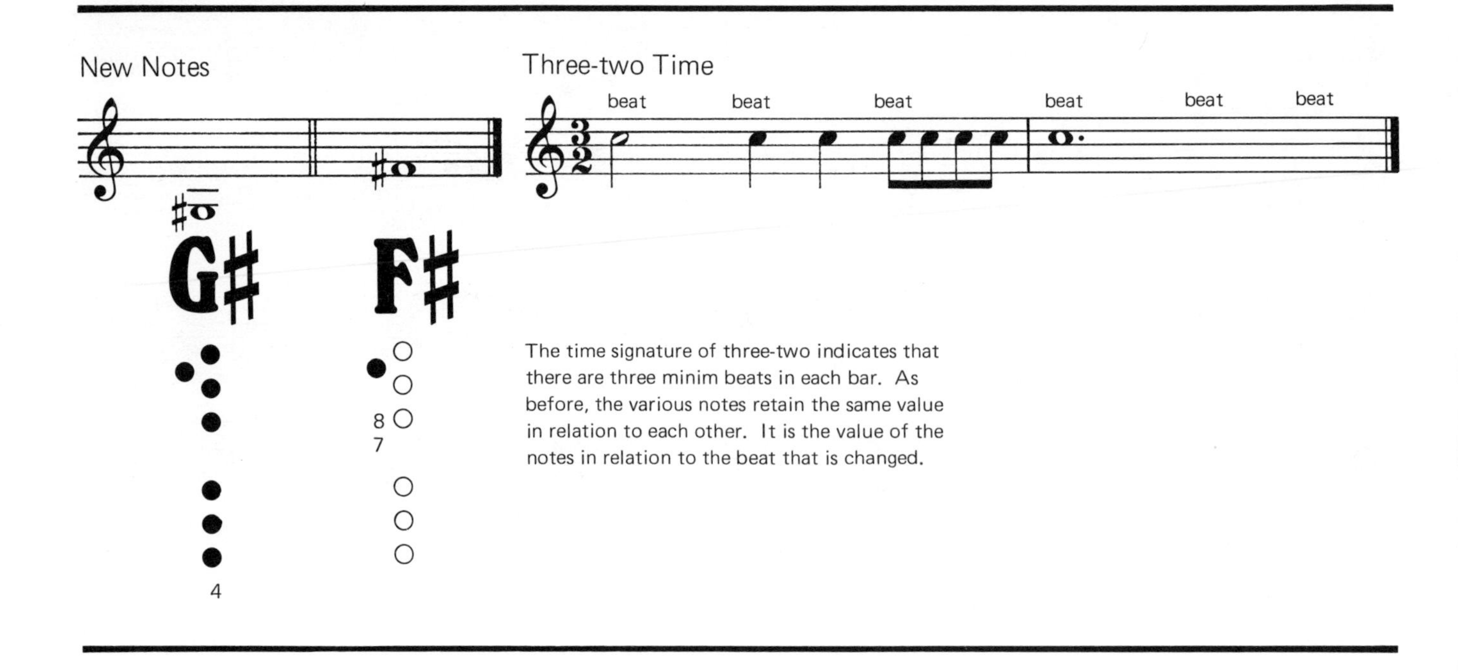


The time signature of three-two indicates that there are three minim beats in each bar. As before, the various notes retain the same value in relation to each other. It is the value of the notes in relation to the beat that is changed.

Finger technique

1. Key 7a is an alternative fingering for lower register D♯. The most important use of this fingering is during a chromatic run; an example can be found in bar 7 of "Andante" by Diabelli.

2. When lower register F♯ occurs during a chromatic run, the fingering given in this unit is the one that is normally used. An example can be found in bar 7 of "Andante" by Diabelli.

# UNIT 24

## Triplets

A triplet can be defined as 'three notes played in the time of two notes of the same value' (for instance, three quavers played in the time of two quavers). The number 3 is placed over or under them to show the momentary change of note value.

## Rests of Several Bars

When a rest of several bars is required, only one bar is used; a black line is usually drawn in this bar and the number of complete bars to be counted placed on top. The example is taken from the concert piece on page 59.

## Exercise

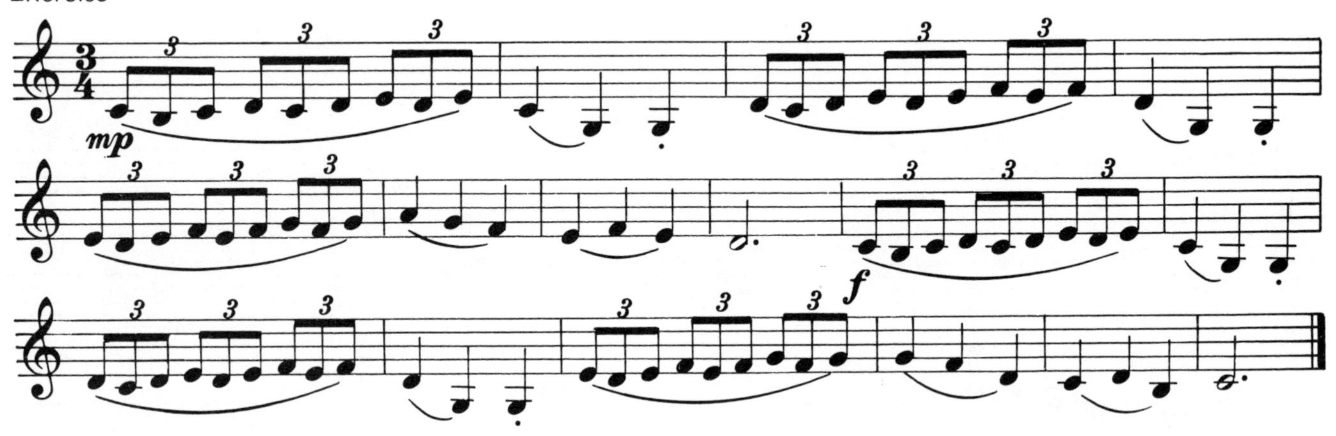


## Scales and arpeggios

C Major, to be played from memory

A Minor (harmonic form) to be played from memory

D Minor (harmonic form) to be played from memory

## Musicianship

Both pieces in this unit have performing directions relating to their mood: the Handel "Aria" is marked dolce espressivo, and the Mozart "Minuet" grazioso. As you practise, try to create these moods, and in particular use the shapes of the phrases for displaying control over the dynamics. In the "Aria", the repeated notes create good opportunities for expressive tenuto playing; the important thing to remember is that performing directions are a starting point for creating your own expression.

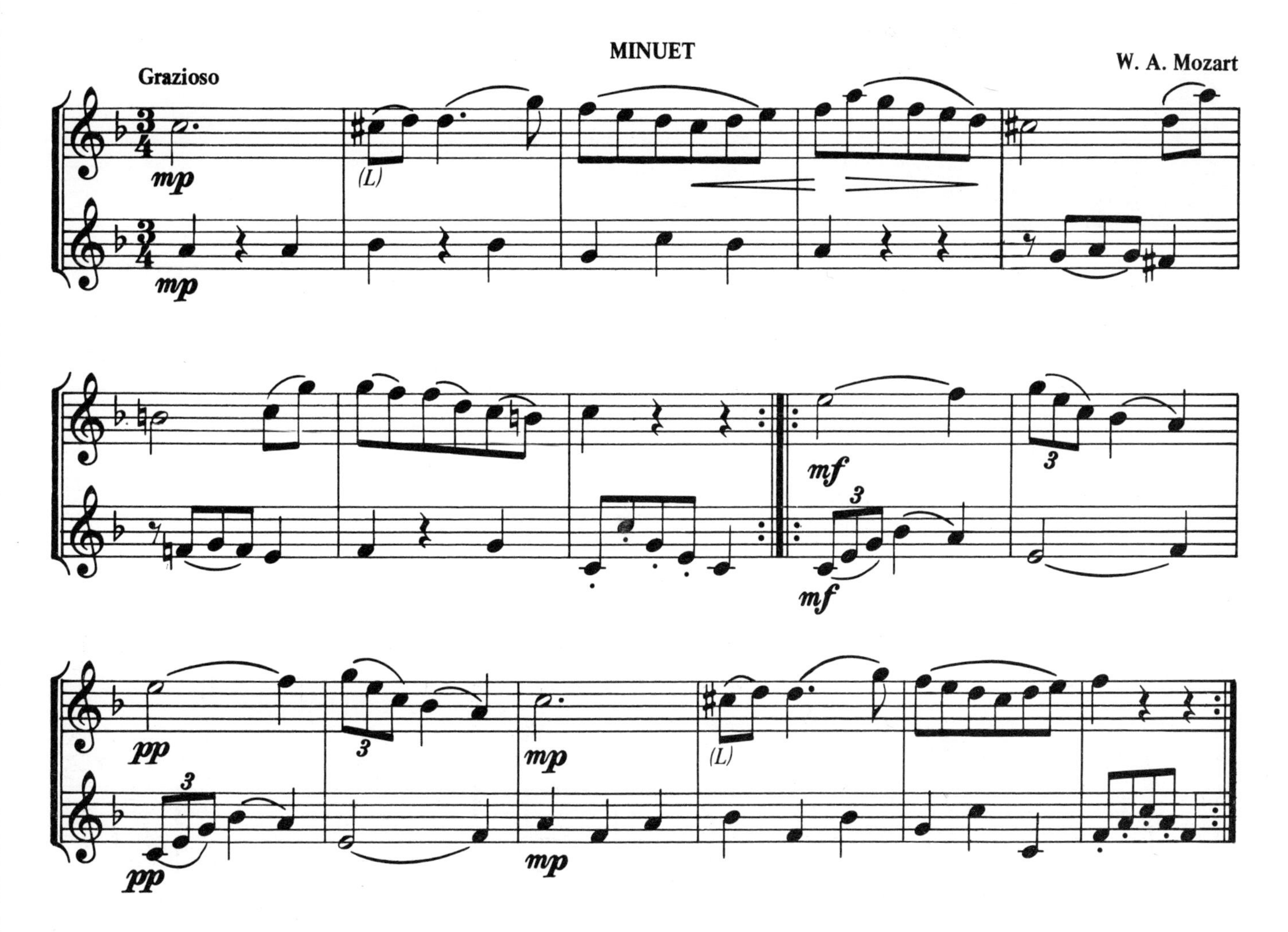

# CONCERT PIECES FOR UNITS 17-24

'Minuet and Trio' by Beethoven, 'Air' by Weber, and 'Carol' by Finzi are examples of music that have been set for early grade examinations.

## LARGO

*from "Sonatina No. 3"*

G. P. TELEMANN
(1681-1767)

arr. PETER WASTALL and DEREK HYDE

# AIR

*from "Der Freischutz"*

CARL MARIA von WEBER
(1786-1826)
arr. PETER WASTALL

# SUBURBAN SUNDAY

KEITH RAMON COLE

# CAROL

*from "Five Bagatelles"*

GERALD FINZI
(1901-1956)

# BASIC FINGERING CHART

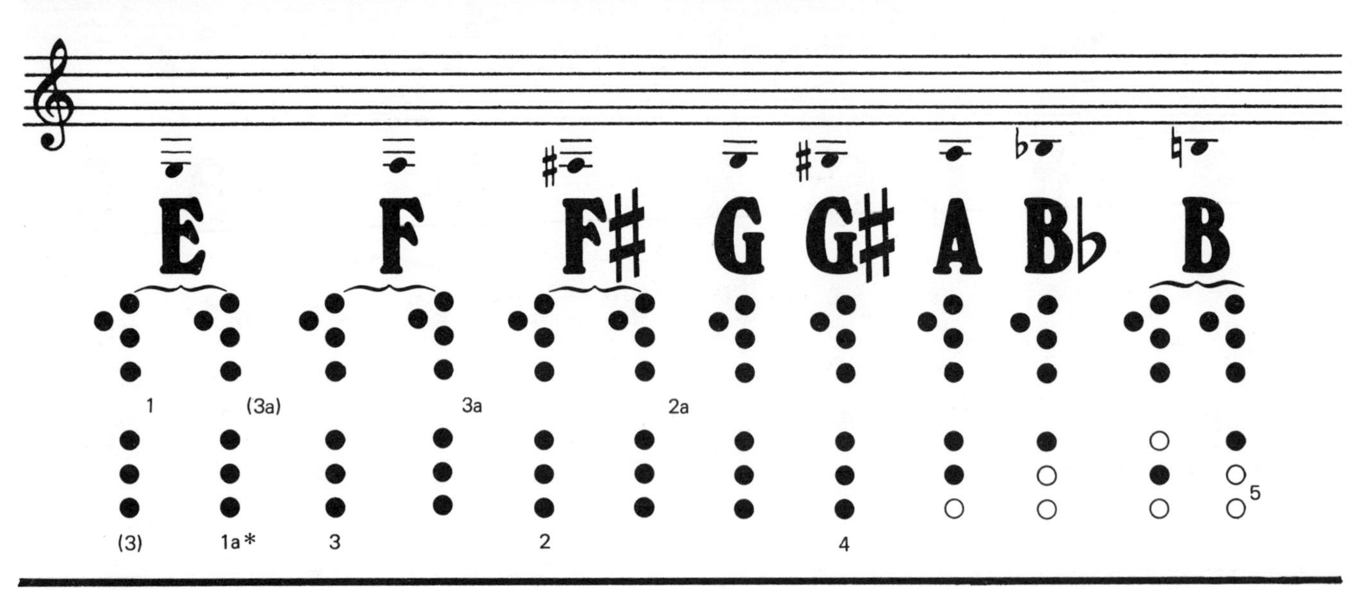


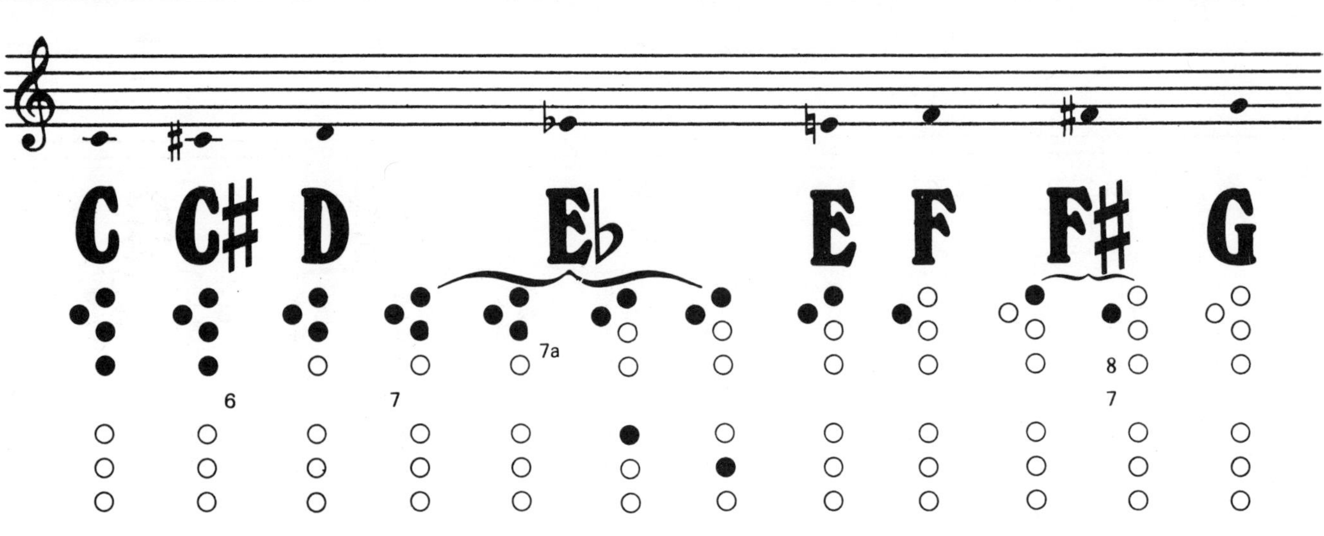


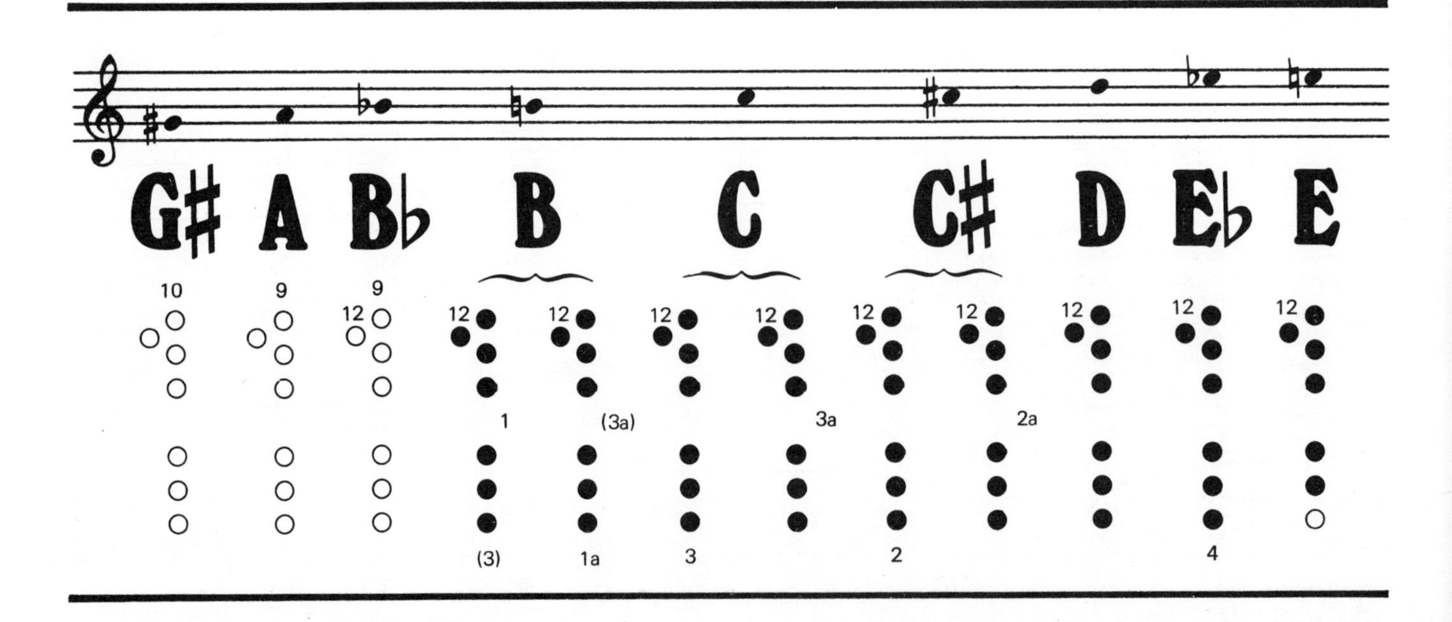

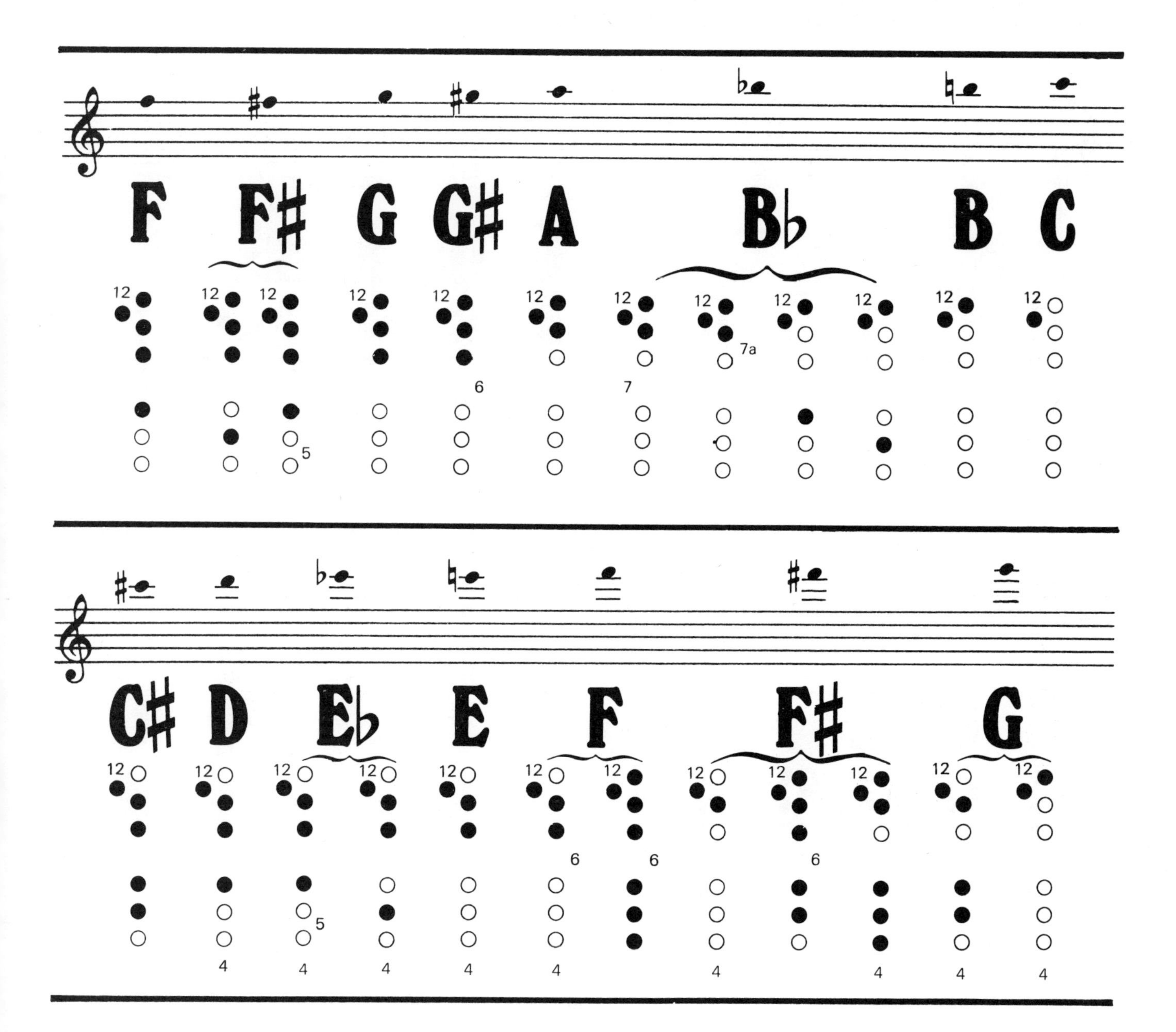


( ) optional

* Keys 1a, 2a and 3a are duplicates of keys 1, 2 and 3 (see units 15 and 17 for detailed technique)

# TIME SIGNATURES

1. Look up the time signature

2. Look in the left hand column to find the number of beats in each bar.

3. Look in the top row above the time signature to find the type of note that equals one beat.

| | Simple time | | | Compound time | | |
|---|---|---|---|---|---|---|
| Value of each beat (type of note) | 𝅗𝅥 | ♩ | ♪ | 𝅗𝅥. | ♩. | ♪. |
| Value of each beat as a fraction of a semibreve | $\frac{1}{2}$ | $\frac{1}{4}$ | $\frac{1}{8}$ | $\frac{3}{4}$ | $\frac{3}{8}$ | $\frac{3}{16}$ |
| 2 beats in each bar | $\frac{2}{2}$ | $\frac{2}{4}$ | $\frac{2}{8}$ | $\frac{6}{4}$ | $\frac{6}{8}$ | $\frac{6}{16}$ |
| 3 beats in each bar | $\frac{3}{2}$ | $\frac{3}{4}$ | $\frac{3}{8}$ | $\frac{9}{4}$ | $\frac{9}{8}$ | $\frac{9}{16}$ |
| 4 beats in each bar | $\frac{4}{2}$ | $\frac{4}{4}$ | $\frac{4}{8}$ | $\frac{12}{4}$ | $\frac{12}{8}$ | $\frac{12}{16}$ |

# ITALIAN TERMS

**A tempo** Resume the normal speed.
**Accelerando** Becoming gradually faster.
**Adagio** Slow, leisurely.
**Agitato** Agitated.
**Alla marcia** In the style of a march.
**Allargando** Broadening out.
**Allegretto** Slightly slower than Allegro.
**Allegro** Lively, reasonably fast.
**Andante** (lit. walking) At a moderate pace.
**Andantino** A little andante.
**Animato** Animated.
**Cantabile** In a singing style.
**Con** With.
**Crescendo** *(cresc.)* Becoming louder.
**Da Capo (D.C.) al Fine** Back to the beginning and finish at the word Fine.
**Dal Segno (D. S.)** From the sign 𝄋
**Deciso** Decisively, firmly.
**Diminuendo** *(dim.)* Becoming gradually softer.
**Dolce** Sweetly.
**E, Ed** And.
**Espressivo** *(espress.)* With expression, with feeling.
**Forte (*f*)** Loud.
**Fortissimo (*ff*)** Very loud.
**Grazioso** Gracefully.
**Giocoso** Humorously.
**Largo** Slow and stately, broad.
**Larghetto** Less slow than Largo.
**Legato** Smoothly.
**Leggiero** Lightly.
**Lento** Slowly.
**Maestoso** Majestically.
**Meno mosso** Less movement.
**Mezzo forte (*mf*)** Moderately loud.
**Mezzo piano (*mp*)** Moderately soft.
**Moderato** Moderate time.
**Molto** Much.
**Moto** Movement.
**Non troppo** Not too much.
**Pianissimo (*pp*)** Very soft.
**Piano (*p*)** Soft.
**Più mosso** More movement, quicker.
**Poco a poco** Little by little (gradually).
**Pomposo** Pompously.
**Presto** Very quick.
**Quasi** As if, almost.
**Rallentando (rall.)** Becoming gradually slower.
**Ritenuto (rit.)** Hold back (slower at once).
**Rubato** Flexibly.
**Semplice** Simple.
**Sempre** Always.
**Sforzando (*sf*, *sfz*)** Forcing, accented.
**Solenne** Solemn.
**Sonore** Sonorous, full toned.
**Sostenuto** Sustained.
**Spirito** Spirit, life, energy.
**Tempo I** Resume the original speed.
**Tenuto** Held.
**Tranquillo** Quietly.
**Un poco** A little.
**Vivace** Lively, quick.

Printed by
Halstan & Co. Ltd., Amersham, Bucks., England